JOHN SHUTTLEWORTH

500

Bus Stops

JOHN SHUTTLEWORTH'S GUIDE TO STARDOM AND OTHER TOP TIPS

500
Bus Stops

CONCEIVED AND WRITTEN BY

GRAHAM FELLOWS

BBC

This book is published to accompany the BBC
television series entitled *500 Bus Stops* which was
first broadcast in 1997.
Executive Producer Peter Symes,
Assistant Producers Will Yapp and Martin Willis,
Director Willy Smax

Published by BBC Books
an imprint of BBC Consumer Publishing
BBC Worldwide Ltd
Woodlands
80 Wood Lane
London W12 OTT

First published 1997

ISBN 0 563 38763 7

Designed by DW Design
Set in New Caledonia and Cooper Black
Printed in Great Britain by
Butler & Tanner Ltd, Frome and London
Cover printed by Belmont Press, Northampton

Contents

ACKNOWLEDGEMENTS

A big thank you to Sheila Ableman for agreeing to pay me to write such nonsense, to Vicky Cribb for her superb advice and increasingly stern (yet always kindly) reminders about deadlines, to Barbara Nash for her experienced eye and delightfully childish faxes (and the pompodums!), to Bobby Birchall for his inspired design, to Jane Coney for wading through all my 'John' piccies, to Will Yapp and Martin Willis for their marvellously swift response to my cries for help and for approaching me in the first place with the idea for the *500 Bus Stops* series, to Willy Smax and Peter Symes for helping us to execute it, to Lucy Day for remembering to bring her camera on location, to my sister Lorna for donning a tasteless flowery top at a moment's notice (and becoming Mary), to my father Derek for last-minute photos (and for being the wonderfully silly man he is), to sole agent Richard Bucknall for his unwavering support (and telephone manner) over the past five years (keep it coming!) and to Kathryn Heywood for only 'thinking' about leaving me during the writing of this book.

PICTURE CREDITS

500 Bus Stops

AUTHOR BIOGRAPHY

Rumour has it that John Shuttleworth doesn't really exist, but is in fact the comic creation of considerably younger actor/musician Graham Fellows who, like John, hails from Sheffield, but now resides in Louth, Lincolnshire with Kathryn Heywood, a teacher, and their daughters Alice and Suzannah.

In 1978, whilst still at drama college in Manchester, Graham wrote and sang the punk classic 'Jilted John' which reached number 4 in the UK charts. His many acting credits include *Coronation Street,* Lynda la Plante's *Comics,* and *Coogan's Run.* He recently voiced all the characters in a forthcoming Aardman animation, *Stagefright.*

The John Shuttleworth phenomenon began life in 1985 as a spoof 'bad demo' tape to amuse a friend in the music business. More tapes and sporadic live performances followed, before the real Ken Worthington entered Graham's life. Impresario and lapsed Buddhist, Richard Bucknall agreed to become Graham's sole agent (for a small fee), and a Perrier nomination at the Edinburgh Fringe in 1992 for *John Shuttleworth's Guide to Stardom* swiftly followed, securing John's minor cult status.

Graham has since written and recorded two series of *The Shuttleworths* for Radio 4, appeared on Channel 4's *Saturday Zoo,* and performed numerous live shows (including playing to 25,000 Blur fans at London's Mile End stadium in 1996).

Graham's hobbies include laughing (affectionately) at struggling retail outlets, imagining what it would be like to do gardening, and eavesdropping on the silly world.

For further information please send an SAE to:
The John Shuttleworth Appreciation Society
P.O.Box 17, Louth, Lincs, LN11 9GF

INTRODUCTION

My name is John Shuttleworth. I'm a versatile singer/songwriter from Sheffield, South Yorkshire, married to Mary, who is a dinner-lady at a local primary school. We've got two teenage children – Darren, nineteen, who works for Victoria Wine, and Karen, fifteen, who plays recorder on some of my demos – including the haunting ballad 'Whitsuntide'.

Oh, and we've got a Scottie dog, called Kirsty, who sits on the *TV Quick*, scampers with her paws and cockles the paper. Do you know what I mean when I say 'cockles'? Well, she rumples it – that's what I mean. In fact, the other day she damaged a nice picture of Blur's Damon Albarn that I was hoping to mount on card at a later date – I was very cross with her about that.

I used to work for Comet, demonstrating audio equipment. I tended to play Kagagoogoo's 'Too Shy', because that was a very good production. We sold a lot of systems on the strength of that one – a lot of Sanyos, a lot of Albas. Oh, and I also played Mac and Katie Cassoon. (Mind you, that was on tape – normal bias, so it was a bit hissy, you know.)

I left Comet to go and work as a security guard for a sweet factory in the Rotherham area. Obviously, I can't say exactly where for security reasons. (Some people think that's a joke when I say that, but it's not.) Anyway, I was made redundant a few years ago, and, with my redundancy pay, I purchased a Yamaha electronic home organ, with built-in auto accompaniment.

Now, I spend my days at the organ, working on my songs, honing them down, and sending my tapes off to pop artistes, such as Five Star, Clannard, Chris Rea, etc. I sent one off to Paul Young recently, but he sent it back. I forgot to put Dolby on, you see, so it was too hissy for him. Ah well!

I would like to thank my next-door neighbour and sole agent, Ken Worthington, for organizing my National Rock Tour of the UK and the TV Rockumentary all on his own. Cheers, Kenny, nice one!

500 Bus Stops

Finally, I'd like to thank you for purchasing this book (I'm giving you the benefit of the doubt and presuming you didn't steal it), which I wrote by hand and recorded on my tape recorder during – and between – bus journeys to and from venues for my National Rock Tour and the making of my TV Rockumentary.

May I also thank you in anticipation that, the next time you're in town doing a big shop, you will seriously consider buying another copy for a friend, relative or colleague (or even ex-colleague – if you're still on good terms with them. Then again, if you're not, well, what an excellent way to heal the rift!).

Bye for now, readers.

God bless,

John Shuttleworth

John Shuttleworth

Arctic Rock'n'Roll

John Shuttleworth's Guide to Stardom and How to Have a Pleasant Marriage

So you want to be a star, do you? Well, don't be embarrassed. You are not alone! Everybody does, if they're honest with themselves. Actually, I can think of one person who doesn't want to be – Ken Worthington, my next-door neighbour and sole agent. That's because he's already had a brush with fame and found it unpleasant. Ken was on *New Faces* in 1973, of course. Yes, he did come last, but it was definitely him, you know. I'll tell you all about that later.

Ken isn't here at the moment. He may have popped out to buy some fun stickers for his bumbag – in readiness for my National Rock Tour of the UK, which commences this afternoon in the reference section of Bakewell Library. I hope they've remembered to put the projector away, or there'll be no room for my organ!

To be honest, I'm a little worried about having to leave my family for four whole days. Am I going to cope without them? Are they, without me? I mean, who's going to polish the children's shoes ready for the morning? Having said that, they're old enough to polish their own shoes, and modern shoes don't require the degree of maintenance shoes did when I was a lad. But what about the DIY jobs still outstanding? I'm sorely tempted to mix up some Polyfilla right now and get cracking, but I'm not allowed to. Ken has insisted I take it extremely easy this morning – stipulating that I don loose-fitting garments and remain in the lounge with a soft drink, and a few nibbles if required (which they certainly are!) – to contemplate the difficult days ahead.

I'd have thought Ken would have been back by now, but he may have been very naughty and popped to the Indian restaurant for an early business lunch (£2.50 without a sweet). Or he may have opted for a takeaway. If so, any moment now, a brown carrier bag will swing into view as Ken returns with his meal. (As I say, there's no sign of him as yet, readers, but rest assured that the second he does show up you'll be the first to know about it. After me, of course!)

In the meantime, let me tell you why I'm writing this book. Firstly, I've always wanted to write a guidebook on stardom. You see, I've picked up quite a few tips over the years – from various people including Ian Wrigley. I don't know if you know him. He does deejaying at the St John's Ambulance Rooms sometimes. And from Ken Worthington, of course, whose showbiz connections are not to be sneezed at. He once travelled on a minibus to Riber Castle with Ken Dodd's niece – well, she was in the minibus behind. (Oo – so it's not that good a connection, that one, is it!). Ken also attended Dana's wedding. He wasn't invited, but he still went along.

'Oh well!' I hear you cry. 'If you know so much about stardom how come you're not a big star yourself?' The simple answer to that is I really don't know, readers. It's not through want of trying, I assure you.

But, after this tour, who knows what will happen? Of course, if I do make it Big Time – and I sincerely hope I do, because I'm no spring chicken and time's running out for me, I realize that – everyone's going to want to know all about me, aren't they? My innermost secrets, etc. (Actually, I'm not telling you those, I'm sorry. But I'll gladly give you advice on bargain-hunting, controlling rowdy youngsters, etc.)

However, once I'm famous I'll be too busy signing autographs and posing for *Hello* magazine, etc., to have any time to write down my thoughts – so it makes sense to do it now, doesn't it? Also, someone ought to keep a record of what happens during this tour. I know Ken's filming it on his camcorder, but he might accidentally tape over it. I wouldn't put it past him.

John Shuttleworth's Guide to Stardom

Now then, readers, before we begin I must stress that not everyone is cut out for stardom. If you think you may be one of those unfortunate souls, then you must abandon this section of the book and all plans for becoming famous right now. If you don't, you're going to become extremely bitter when it doesn't happen to you. You'll also queer the pitch for genuine artistes like myself. It's blinking frustrating to see youngsters with no talent whatsoever jumping the queue, so to speak. I've written a song all about that. It goes like this:

These kids in tracksuits and training shoes
They make me angry, they really do
They've rapped their way into the nation's hearts
Straight off the street and into the charts

They think they're poets but they can't even speak
They display no knowledge of microphone technique
They're making millions when they should be in fact
Working the club circuit, honing their act

I wrote a letter once to Radio 1 Disc Jockey, John Peel – because he's doing nothing to discourage these poor-quality acts, is he, and I thought he needed putting right on a few matters. This is actually the first of several letters I'm planning on printing in this book. I wasn't going to bother, but Ken says it's what proper writers do – collect their letters together and then publish them – so, you know, why not? Unfortunately, there were no replies to any of them – well, none that are fit to publish! Why do people have to be so rude – I don't know! Anyway, here's the letter I wrote to John Peel:

500 Bus Stops

6th June, 1986

Dear Mr Peel,

To be perfectly frank, I don't think much of the music you play on your show. I've often – whilst waiting for Brian Matthews's Around Midnight *– caught the end of your programme, and I must say I'm dismayed by the standard of some of the groups I hear. I gather that, like myself, you're no spring chicken, so what is it about Barbra Streisand that prevents you from giving her discs the occasional spin? Is it her big nose? I hope that's not the reason, especially since it's not that big any more, anyway. Or Abba – those great Swedish ambassadors of Pop. Were you bullied as a child by someone with blond hair? I don't know, John, I'm baffled, I don't mind admitting it.*

Anyway, I've had my moan. I realize that if I go on too much it might turn you against me, and then you might not listen to the enclosed audio cassette which is a collection of my finest songs to date. Please feel free to give it a whirl on your programme.

Whilst I'm about it, may I have a request for my wife, Mary? Anything melodic would be splendid. I realize yours is an up-tempo show so how about 'Green Door' by Shaky – the brilliant Welsh balladeer who has slipped so effortlessly into the shoes of the King.

I'll be tuning in regularly from now on, John. (Just in case!)

Kind regards to your family,

John Shuttleworth (Mr)

Now, before we go any further, readers, I must just tell you the Five Essential Don'ts For Aspiring Artistes. I can't remember them all, but anyway...

1. Don't get poorly

Keep yourself in tiptop condition – sleek and well groomed. Have a jacket potato for your tea, and eat plenty of greens, cane sugar, that sort of thing. For your pudding you could have a Tracker bar (kinder to the environment) or a fromage frais, because they're fibre-based, aren't they?

Here's a tip: keep a fun-size Topic or Lion bar in your tunic for when you get low on energy during your performance.

'Excuse me, John!'

'Ken! Yes, what is it?' (I'm sorry, readers, I didn't notify you about Ken's arrival like I promised. All I can say in my defence is that I didn't see him until a second ago, because I had my head down, writing.)

'Remember to turn away from the audience, John, before you have a bite, or everybody will want some!'

'Yes, thanks, Ken. Good point.'

'Thank you, John. Hmm – you know, ladies and gentlemen, I was once at a Mediaeval Banquet in Youlgreave hosted by – '

'I'm sorry, Ken, I am going to have to ask you to stop right there, because we haven't really come to your bit in the book yet.'

'Oh, I see. Would you like me to leave, John?'

'No, Ken. I'd be devastated if you did that. I want you to remain on the premises. All I ask is that you sit in absolute silence, until called upon to speak. Is that fair?'

'It's very fair, John.'

'Good. Now why don't you go and pop your curry on a plate while I tell the readers the next essential Don't.

500 Bus Stops

2. **Don't get depressed**

There's nothing a casting agent or club steward wants to hear less than an artiste saying they feel a bit down or that they've had a bad week. You've got to be up and bubbly at all times in this game. When you arrive for your audition walk with a little swagger, and possibly be chewing a piece of gum. Oo, no, that's a bit slovenly that, isn't it? Erm – Maybe just waggle your head from side to side a few times, if you want to.

    'Mm – I'm not so sure, John.'

    I know, readers! Rub your hands together as if it's a bit cold (though chances are it'll be lovely and warm), then finish with a big clap and say 'Whey-hey-hey! Now then sirrah!' or something a bit silly like that. (They love all that – bookers and impresarios.)

3. **Don't get too excited**

On the opening night of the South Yorkshire Amateur Operatic Society's production of *Aïda* – in which I played an Ethiopian slave – two young lads from Rotherham – also slaves – were doing kung fu in the dressing room (which they shouldn't have been doing, of course). Because they were so excited about the show their timing was a bit off, and one of them accidentally kicked my duffel bag which contained a flask with some oxtail soup inside it. Before I could tell him off he had banged his head on a coat peg. It could have been really nasty, like the end of *Midnight Express*, but luckily there was just slight grazing. But the point is we missed our first entrance where the soldiers turn on us. So the message is: Keep calm. It's just not worth it!

4. **Don't take drugs**

I had a long chat about this with my brother-in-law, Carl, who used to be in the hippies. (He's a butcher now, incidentally and happily married.) Well, Carl said 'Forget it, John. You don't need them'. The problem was that I most certainly did need drugs in order to write a drug-inspired lyric for my song 'Voodoo Lady', which has a baggy beat and would be a nice fun track for Clannard, or erm – What's-it and Jerome.

Trouble is, they're illegal, aren't they – drugs? Besides, I wouldn't know where to obtain any – despite having worked with youngsters with drug-related problems. So, do you know what I did? Well, I drank a four-pack of Hofmeister lager in one sitting – that's what I did. Tell a lie, I had three and I gave one to Ken.

'Didn't I, Ken?'

'You did, John, and I'm mighty grateful to you!'

'Well, you don't need to be, Ken. It was only a can of lager. How's your nan by the way?'

'Erm – she's dead, John. Oh – I see what you mean! It's lovely, thanks. Do you want some?'

'No, thanks, Ken. I'll be having my sandwiches once we've hit the road. Mary's preparing them at this very moment.'

'She isn't actually, John. She's defrosting the fridge.'

'Oh, I see – '

Anyway, readers, suffice it to say my three cans gave me the heightened state of awareness required to complete the psychedelic lyric – and with no risk of dirty needles or HIV positive.

Oo, I've just remembered the fifth essential Don't. Just in time, too!

5. Don't become a big head

So, readers, you've been recognized from that Venture Scout Disco, or from your performance in the foyer of the local swimming baths – so what? Big deal! For goodness' sake don't go all snooty and zoom off in your big flashy motor. Stick around for a while, sign a few autographs. Ask the punters where they hail from, and put them at their ease by inquiring whether they've got any brothers or sisters.

By the way, when you're first recognized, put on a look of shocked surprise – if you want to – and then suddenly break into a big reassuring smile. Perhaps then you could do a quick spoof tap routine or something. The punters deserve that, don't they?

Some stars are lovely, there's no doubt about it. Les Gray from Mud, for example. We saw him a few years ago at the Happy Eater – you know that one on the A1 just before you turn off for Newark – yes, that one. Anyway, he was filling his car up with petrol – he only had an Allegro, I couldn't believe it, but, no, he seemed happy enough. He was doing the Tiger Feet Stomp, and everyone was going 'Les, Les!' you know, and punching the air. It was wonderful. Because of course, people remember the stars from that period, don't they? It's not like nowadays, you don't know who they are.

So – I'll say it one more time, readers, in case the message still hasn't hit home – *Don't become a big head!* If you make it, that is. Some of you won't. But you know that, don't you? Oo, no, I shouldn't have said that. It might shatter your confidence when you're at a most vulnerable stage. Sorry. You might make it, you don't know. Look, I hope you do, and I hope I do as well.

Sadly, some who do climb the ladder of fame to its highest rung abuse their privileged position, by being snooty, or behaving in a mean-spirited way. And this makes you wonder – do the stars remember? Now there's a cue for a song if ever I heard one!

Do The Stars Remember?
(Words and music by J. Shuttleworth)

I put a bandage on a little boy's knee (which little boy?)
The lead singer of Def Leppard – he lived near me
He slipped on some ice at the end of our drive
If it wasn't for me he might now not be alive

But do the stars remember
As the thronging masses cheer
The little people who helped them
On the road to their chosen career?

I stopped a bus for Sebastian Coe
He couldn't catch it for he was too slow
So I put my hand out and caused it to stop
As Seb got on he said 'Phew, thanks a lot!'

(Everybody – with harmonies, if you can do harmonies.
If you can't then please don't or it'll sound horrible)

Do the stars remember
As the thronging masses cheer
The little people who helped them
On the road to their chosen career?

'We can't hear you!' Too far away.

'Watch that tooth!' Far too close.

So, there you have it – the Five Essential Don'ts for Aspiring Artistes. But wait! That's not quite the full story. Haven't we forgotten something?

'I don't think so, John.'

'Well, you're very, very wrong, Ken, and it's a bit worrying that you don't realize it – you being my sole agent and everything.'

'Go on then, what have we forgotten, John?'

'Can't you guess? All right, I'll tell you then – '

Microphone technique

Whether you want to be an MC at a trade fair or a close-up magician with patter both topical and blue, a thorough knowledge of microphone technique is essential, otherwise people will think your act is a bit ropy.

It's very important not to get too close to the microphone, or you might chip your tooth on the grill. This happened to me a couple of years ago at a garden party which was held to raise money to send poorly youngsters to Disneyworld. (We didn't raise enough, actually, so we had to take them to the Abbeydale Industrial Hamlet for the day. I drove the minibus.) I was singing Men At Work's 'Do You Come From The Land Downunder?' (They've gone a bit quiet, haven't they?) And on that bit about the Vegemite sandwich I got too close and chipped my tooth on the mike grill. It was my own fault. I was being a bit cocky. But you mustn't get too far away from the mike or you'll be lost under the sound of audience chatter. Tell you what, study the step-by-step guide below. All the information you require is contained there. (Just remember to

The optimum distance. (Note the right hand stylishly grasping the mike lead.)

Advanced technique. (Notice the ring about to playfully strike the microphone chassis whilst the vocalist cleverly maintains eye contact with his audience.)

put the mike back in the stand when you've finished, ready for the next person. Thanks!)

Of course, some performers don't need a microphone. Classically trained vocalists – such as Sir Harry Secombe – just use the natural reverb of the church grounds, or the shopping arcade.

Actually, there's a few more things we've forgotten...

Have you had your publicity piccys done yet?

No? Well, get cracking. Go to the woods and get some nice shots of yourself crouching in the undergrowth. (Unless it's damp underfoot. In these circumstances have one leg cocked up on a tree stump, with your back slightly arched and your hands placed upon your hips.) If you're a lady, you might consider hiring a Sergeant Pepper tunic for the session, and investing perhaps in a pot of orange blusher.

Ask the printer to put your 'parts played' in a little star next to your head – as I've done in mine. If you've not performed any amateur work then just put whatever you played at school in the nativity play in the star. You know, 'Fourth Shepherd' or whatever. Or, if you weren't lucky enough to have been chosen for the nativity play, you surely must have played in the street when you were little – 'Kings and Queens', that sort of thing. Well, put it down in your little star, because, believe me, it's still valid.

What about your CV?

Yes, it's time now to get your CV typed up. Find a friend with an electric typewriter, if possible. I borrow the one from the halfway house near us, and in return I have to mow their lawn. In fact, I'm using it now to write this book. Thanks, Linda! (I meant to thank her in the Introduction, but I forgot – sorry Linda!)

For guidance on CV layout have a glimpse at my CV (printed opposite with my full consent). Obviously the complete document runs to several pages, but this brief extract will give you some useful pointers.

My publicity photo, complete with friendly personal greeting.

NAME: *John Shuttleworth*

OCCUPATION: *Well, I used to be a security guard for a sweet factory in the Rotherham area, and before that I worked for Comet. Currently, I'm a versatile singer/songwriter operating from a private address in Sheffield, South Yorkshire*

PARTS PLAYED: *Wishee Washee in* Aladdin *at Dinnington Alhambra; Ethiopian Slave in the South Yorkshire Amateur Operatic Society's production of* Aïda *in 1974. More recently, I dearly wanted to be a passer-by in Central TV's excellent* Peak Practice, *because I know the local terrain, and would have been very sure-footed, you know. But when the casting lady asked me if I was in Equity I had to come clean and admit that, alas, I wasn't. (We're with Friends Provident, you see.)*

SPECIAL SKILLS: Swimming underwater, although to be honest I haven't attempted it for a while (there's always too many kiddies in the shallow end). DIY, ping-pong

AMBITION: To become successful in the sphere of popular music

AGENT: Next-door neighbour, Ken Worthington (better known as 'TV's Clarinet Man')

FAVOURITE COLOUR: Fawn

So, readers, you've submitted your CV and photo, had your audition, been offered that nostalgic sing-along at the end of April – you'll be wanting to know your next move, I warrant?

First of all, check that you're not busy at the end of April. You might have promised to shift a sofa for somebody, or received an invite to a friend's caravan that weekend. If it's the second one, then clearly you'd be a fool not to turn down the engagement, although, before you do, you should try and get them to postpone the event. (Bear in mind this might not always be possible: trestle tables may have been booked; access to the tea urn may be restricted to that afternoon, etc.)

Sole representation

Assuming you are free to accept the engagement, you will need somebody to negotiate some petrol money for you. If there's a small fee involved, too, then 'Wow! Congratulations!'. But, in my experience, this is an extremely rare occurrence – and becoming rarer, as the recession bites ever deeper.

. I'm not saying you wouldn't get the petrol money yourself. It really depends on whether there's anyone about at the end of the show. Some of the staff at old folks' homes and hospices are very busy people, and become quite aggressive when challenged in the corridor. Moreover, if most of the audience wandered back to their rooms during your performance (and it's likely that they will – unless you're prepared to do pop standards such as Jennifer Rush, Foreigner, that sort of thing), the staff will be too tied up trying to get them back out again for their afternoon tablets to be bothering with the likes of you.

In cases like these, a sole agent comes in very handy – you can get an ordinary agent if you want, but a 'sole' one sounds better, doesn't it? Not that having one guarantees success. Look at me. Mind you, look at Ken. (I can be rude about him now because he's nipped round to his house to get some mango chutney. I wish he'd taken his curry with him. The aroma's clashing terribly with Mary's Morning Meadow air freshener.)

How I met Ken Worthington

It's a tragic tale, in parts, but the ending is quite uplifting, and may even have you punching the air in a state of euphoria. I hope so, anyway.

In 1970 my first wife, Margaret, died tragically. Four years later I decided to commemorate the anniversary of her death by composing a little verse and submitting it to the local paper, for inclusion in the 'In Memoriam' section. As I recall the poem went something like this:

My wife died in 1970
Peacefully in her sleep
Though she's just a distant memory
Occasional tears I weep

Now, unbeknownst to me, readers, that verse was spotted by Ken Worthington, who at the time was living in a caravan in the Dronfield Woodhouse area. Down on his luck, eking out a meagre existence on just a few items he had left in his larder – as we shall hear directly from Ken's mouth in a later chapter – Ken, or 'TV's Clarinet Man' as he was known to media moguls, admired my poem. So much so that he cut it out and placed it in a small brown envelope for safekeeping, because – as he told me years later – he'd earmarked me a potential song lyricist. Now, I had no knowledge of this, whatsoever. No knowledge.

Why was Ken at such a low ebb? Because he came last on the TV talent show *New Faces*, in 1973. Those of you who caught Ken's appearance will remember it all too vividly. For those younger readers who were taking full advantage of that sunny evening by playing outside on their spacehoppers, Ken wore a glittery tunic, buccaneer's boots and a cape. But I don't think he had a sword. Did he? No, I'm sure he didn't have a sword.

His act involved a tap routine whilst playing the clarinet, and spiralling ever closer to his wife – at the time – Rhiannon. (She, of course, was in a big wicker chair, playing the harp.) Then, just as he got to the epicentre, Ken had to sweep away, and deny her. It was a nice idea – like Hansel and Gretel, or something – and it was working well. But then – he ruined it.

The camera came in for a close-up, and, instead of just doffing his cap at the lens like you or I would do, he sort of – (oo, now I'm in trouble, because it's not the sort of thing you can describe in words. But I'll have a go.) He lifted his hands and, waggling his fingers in the air, opened his eyes very wide, as if he'd seen a ghost. But it was obvious he hadn't – so, why, oh why, did he do it? I don't know, and, to this day, neither does Ken. It destroyed the atmosphere he'd built up, and Tony Hatch crucified him. Honestly, I've never seen Tony so angry. He was so angry a bit of saliva appeared at the side of his mouth, and a bubble, too; though it popped almost as soon as it had formed.

Ken went bright red. I only had a black-and-white telly at the time, but I could see he was crimson. This is why Ken can't appear in my TV Rockumentary, readers, but must remain behind the camera at all times. He's lost his bottle, which is terribly sad, yes. But the thing you have to remember is that not everybody is cut out to appear in public, or is able to string words together in a high-pressure situation like a civic walkabout or a nostalgic sing-along in the St John's Ambulance Rooms.

These are the sort of bookings I imagine Ken will have lined up for me on this tour – though I'm only guessing. He's being very secretive about the whole affair.

That's actually another essential Don't, isn't it? Don't go red! Especially if you're playing a character in a play who's been very poorly and requires a sickly complexion at all times, because it'll look silly, won't it? If you think you are going to go red then (a) Wear a large floppy hat cocked over one eye (b) Carry a fan with you to hide behind.

'The same one that you've got your lines pasted on the back of, John?'

'Aha! You're back, Ken, are you? I'm in the middle of telling your life story.'

'I see – well, wouldn't it be better if I told it, John?'

'Mm – not really, Ken, no. You eat your curry before it goes cold. Then, again, perhaps it's already too cool for human consumption, Ken, in which case you may care to warm it through in our family microwave.'

'Thanks, John. Yes, I will.'

'Don't forget to transfer your meal to a non-metallic dish prior to reheating – otherwise there'll be sparks flying, Ken.'

'I won't, John, don't worry.'

Anyway, readers, a couple of years after his disastrous appearance on *New Faces*, Ken Worthington became my next-door neighbour. I remember the occasion vividly. It was a Sunday night and I was watching *The Brothers* – the classic seventies serial about the family haulage business – with a lamb dinner on my lap (including all the veg, trimmings, etc.). Mary, my wife – I'd married again by this time, of course – came in from the garden and said 'That bloke from *New Faces* has moved in next door'. And I knew who she meant, you know.

We went outside, and, sure enough, there was Ken under his carport, watching the sunset. Initially, I thought he was eating a packet of sparklers. But it was a Curlywurly. They'd only just come out, and we'd never had a chocolate bar like it before, had we? You know, the

'Is he in?' Me pointing at Ken's lounge window. (See how his conifer is beginning to encroach on my land – that's illegal, of course.)

packaging was very unfamiliar. Blimey, I thought, he's eating a packet of sparklers! And I obviously kept my distance. But, no, I soon realized it was a Curlywurly, and advanced once more.

Leaning over the fence I said 'Excuse me, were you on *New Faces* in '73, because me and my wife feel certain that you were?' He didn't answer, but I knew it was him, because he wheeled round and did that same face – you know, as if he'd seen a ghost. Well, to be fair, I think I startled him.

'You did, John, yes.'

Within seconds we were talking about showbusiness. Ken had become an impresario by this time and, having recovered from his setback, landed a plum job with Eagle Star Insurance. (He retired

500 Bus Stops

recently, incidentally, with a nice fat pension – though this hasn't prevented him from being a bit stingy at times.)

'What do you mean, John? I'm about to take you on an all-expenses-paid tour of Great Britain!'

'I'm sorry, Ken, I completely forgot about that.'

'In fact, we'd better get cracking or we'll be late for the sound check at Bakewell Library.'

'In a minute, Ken. I'm just coming to the exciting bit.'

'Oh, good!'

Well, readers, when I told Ken I was a songwriter he produced a scruffy brown envelope which he said contained some wonderful lyrics and asked would I be interested in trying to compose some music to fit? 'Certainly,' I said. Well, when I discovered it was the poem I'd written about my first wife there were some tears, initially, because I'd lost my copy. And when I realized I'd be getting all the royalties as both lyric and tune writer, I was on cloud nine.

Ken and I drove into Derbyshire for a couple of lagers. We had a lovely time, exchanging showbusiness anecdotes, and cracking jokes of a mildly bawdy nature. Did we overstep the mark at any point? Maybe so, as I recall an ashtray got accidentally broken in a pub in Foolow.

Ken is now my sole agent – as I've already stated – and I'm extremely satisfied with the job he does. Sometimes. On occasions he annoys me because he doesn't seem that bothered about furthering my career, and will, for example, say a song of mine is rubbish when really he's not had time to digest the lyric.

'I only did that once, John.'

'Yes, but the memory lingers, Ken. You hurt me badly with your barbed comments.'

'I'm sorry John. I'm going home now anyway. I've forgotten to pack my bumbag for the tour.'

'Wait, Ken. You must stay with us. We need you for the next item, which is – '

How to make a demo with special guest Ken Worthington

'Welcome, Ken.'

'Thank you, John. It's good to be here.'

This section, readers, is obviously of particular interest to people like myself because, being a versatile singer/songwriter, I often need to make a demo of my latest composition.

'So tell us, Ken. What do you do then?'

'I'm an impresario, John.'

'Yes I know, Ken, but, you know – erm – how do you make a demo?'

'Well – erm – '

'Actually, Ken, sorry to interrupt you, but, before you begin, I should just tell the readers how *not* to make a demo.'

'Oh, I see – yes, that's a good idea, John.'

'Yes, Ken, and I'm going to do that by simply showing them another of my letters.'

Believe it or not, readers, I heard this demo on BBC Radio 3, of all places. (I'm assuming it was a demo. I can't believe it was a proper posh recording.) Anyway, hearing it was a terrible experience, which I feel I must share with you all:

Above we see the eye-catching cover of an instructional audio cassette I issued to fellow songwriters as a Christmas gift. Clever, don't you think?

3rd November, 1991

Dear Radio 3,

It is with deep regret that I must join the growing tide of public anger aimed at your music station. Incidentally, I'm not a fan anyway, and it was only by accident (whilst searching for the 5 p.m. weather forecast on Radio 2 last Tuesday), that I stumbled upon the most awful racket I have ever heard on public radio.

A woman singing (well, groaning would be more accurate) unintelligibly in Japanese, and totally out of key, to an accompaniment of poor-quality mandolin and recorder – both of which sounded like they were being played by toddlers who were just messing about, i.e. not following any strict musical notation.

Now don't get me wrong. I'm not anti-Jap or anything. I enjoy Chinese food, and Sumo wrestling has captured my imagination as much as everyone else's, but I really can't let such shoddy broadcasting go unchecked.

What are you playing at, Radio 3? Come on, pull your socks up!

Yours sincerely,

J. Shuttleworth (Mr)

'Sorry about that interruption, Ken.'

'No, you're right, John. It needed to be said. It did.'

'Please continue, Ken. Tell us then – how do you go about making a quality demonstration recording?'

'Well, John. First of all you should make sure that all the windows are closed.'

'I see. Right. Then what, Ken?'

'Then you should turn the telly down.'

'Erm – surely off, Ken.'

'Well, yes, in an ideal world, John.'

'Of course, it's not always possible. Please continue, Ken. What do we do then?'

'Erm – press record.'

'Or play and record at the same time sometimes, isn't it, Ken?'

'Granted, yes!'

'Yes – I caught you out there then, Ken, didn't I?'

'You did, John!'

'Okay, but let's be serious again for a second, Ken. You missed something out, I'm afraid.'

'What was that, then, John?'

'You failed to tell the readers to clean their tape heads before commencing the recording session – and the best method of doing this.'

'Oh, that's easy, John. You just take a cotton rag, douse it in soapy water, and then rub – '

'Erm, excuse me, Ken! I'm sorry, but I'm going to have to stop you right there, because that's exactly what you *don't* do, Ken. You don't do that to your tape heads, do you?'

'I do, John.'

'I can't believe it, Ken. Who told you to do that?'

'I can't remember, John. Somebody.'

'They're crazy. You know, you'll damage the equipment if you do that.'

'No, you won't.'

'You will, Ken. If I'd known you were going to say that I wouldn't have asked you to present the item.'

'I'm sorry, John. What should you do then?'

'You should use isopropyl alcohol and cottonbuds.'

'Oh! Well, nobody told me that, John. Nobody told me!'

Oh dear, readers! I've had to take a little break to get over the shock of what Ken just said. I can't believe it. I'm not sure he can either. He left the premises a couple of minutes ago looking ever so sheepish, and shaking a bit. He seemed genuinely shocked that he got it wrong – but he did, didn't he? He was very wide of the mark there.

How to do acting

There's a lass who every day walks past our house very slowly. At first, because she kept stopping by the wall, looking down and smiling, I thought she was admiring my pointing. But by the time she'd reached the gate I realized she was merely taking her little boy for a walk. Anyway, I reckon this lass has got the right face to play a nurse in *Casualty*, who perhaps steals some money from a friend. (Though obviously she'd give it her back at the end of the episode.)

There's a chap walking past right now who'd be ideal as a video-store owner in *Taggart* – No, I beg your pardon, a sniper in *Bergerac*. Yes, definitely.

Do you get the idea? Now go and have a look in the mirror and decide what part you could convincingly play on the telly. Once you've decided, don loose-fitting garments, find a warm quiet space and practise the following acting lesson.

How to make a phone call for the small screen

It's quite tricky teaching you this, readers, without actually being by your side to guide your hands as you manoeuvre the handset from the cradle to your ear. The important thing to remember is to speed up the action, otherwise you'll lose the viewers' attention. Don't wait for ages to get

Arctic Rock 'n' Roll

through (even though you would normally). If it's bad news you're about to receive, act as if you're really happy – laughing in a carefree manner as you pick up the receiver – then wait for a moment, then stop laughing and hunch your shoulders slightly. If it's a party you're calling from and a drunken fellow guest is trying to pass you a drink, dissuade them by flapping your hand rapidly. (You might ask them to turn down the music, too, but, before you do, consider whether you want everyone to become as miserable as you've just become.)

The most important thing to remember is, at the end of the call, look at the receiver for a second, prior to replacing it in the cradle. Some professional actors don't do this I've noticed, and that annoys me because you can't see their dramatic intention.

There's quite a lot to take in there, I realize that, and after your first few attempts I'm sure you'll be cursing me. But stick with it, it'll get easier.

I'd have liked to tell you how to exit from a restaurant when you're angry, because there's a lot involved there. (You've got to throw your napkin down, and bump into a waiter on the way out.) But there's no time now because I'm a bit behind this morning with my packing for the tour.

I'll leave you with the words of the great man himself, Tarby. Ken met him once at a Mediaeval Banquet in Youlgreave – it was to raise money to buy boxing gloves for under-privileged youngsters – and, as Tarby was replenishing Ken's goblet, he said – (oo, I've forgotten now. Fortunately, Ken's just come back.)

'Ken, what did Tarby say to you? Oh – ? Are you all right, Ken?'

'Yes, thanks, John.'

'You've not been weeping, have you?'

'I have not!'

'It's just that you look a bit glassy-eyed. And your hair could do with a comb.' (In fact, readers, the way Ken's looking at the moment he'd be very convincing as a drugs baron in *Spender*.) 'Where've you been, Ken?'

'I've been having a glass of milk, John.'

'I see. Anyway, what did Tarby say to you? Please tell us, we're dying to know.'

'Mary, my wife? Knocked down by a bus? Which number?'

'Well, John – he said "If it happens for you, it's a great life. If it doesn't happen for you, it's still a great life".'

'Really? Is that what he said, Ken? That sounds a bit stupid, that, Ken, if you don't mind me saying. How can it be a great life if it doesn't happen for you?'

'I wouldn't worry about it, John, because it will happen for you. You're about to do a National Rock Tour of significant venues in the UK. You're going to be a star!'

'Oo, Ken, do you think so?'

'Yes, but don't get too excited, just in case it doesn't happen.'

'You don't need to tell me that, Ken. Or the readers. We know that already – it's the third essential Don't. By the way, there's six now. Hey, where are you going, Ken?'

'I've got things to do, John. Once my bumbag's packed I've got to nip to Texas to buy a notice board.'

'Why don't you go to Homebase, Ken? It's nearer.'

'Is that meant to be a joke, John?'

'No – it's definitely nearer, Ken.'

I'm in the garage now, readers, having a final practice on my organ before Ken and I embark on my first National Rock Tour of the UK. I'm practising a piece that employs Trombone 2, but, in my excitement, I keep catching the fun rhythm with my knuckles. That's not such a tragedy! After all, the fun rhythm is a glorious sound, like two yapping dogs (one big one and one little one) and it goes down especially well in sheltered accommodation, hospices, etc., because it cheers them up, you know.

'Barking mad!' Kirsty expresses interest in my organ's fun rhythm.

You may be wondering, readers, why I'm set up in the garage. It's because I've been banned from the lounge. It was interfering with the telly, you see, which is fair enough, I suppose. But I'm very happy here – in fact, I'm going to miss it on the tour. There's a nice reverb off the breeze blocks, and the deep freeze is just the right height at which to operate my keyboard. My seat is a twenty-four pack of Diet Sprite which gets lower, of course, as the cans are transferred to the kitchen for domestic consumption. But I don't mind that – I quite enjoy the challenge of having to reach ever higher, you know.

Now, you are doubtless wondering how we are going to travel on this tour. Well, the answer is very simple – in my Austin Ambassador. It's a Y reg. It has a beige body with a chocolate brown interior. There've been three sets of mats since I owned the vehicle, and the light's gone in the glove compartment – I know these facts aren't very interesting on their own, but, collectively, there's quite a tale, I'm sure you'll agree.

After all, it's got a full service history, but unfortunately there isn't time to tell you that now. Instead, why don't I just sing you the song I wrote in praise of the vehicle, shall I? Yes, but, after that, I'll have to close for a while because we're about to set off to Bakewell and obviously I can't be writing while I'm driving.

'Ready for off!' Posing against the rear of my Austin Ambassador, Y reg.

My Austin Ambassador Y reg, Y reg, Y reg
My Austin Ambassador Y reg is a car that I revere
My Austin Ambassador Y reg, Y reg, Y reg
Don't keep asking me why, Reg
It just happens to be that year

Now you may covet a Clio
Or a Mondeo
Marvel at the Montego
Fine but not me, no

Now you may be utterly sold on
Your Peugeot, your Proton
Your Mitsubishi Shogun
But I'll always dote on

My Austin Ambassador Y reg, Y reg, Y reg etc.

I'd even say no ter
A Rolls with a chauffeur
A brand new Toyota
A Skoda? Give over!

I've got an Austin Ambassador Y reg, Y reg, Y reg
Don't keep asking me why, Reg
It just happens to be that year

Readers, something terrible has happened. The official tour vehicle, my car – the one I've just been singing about in such glowing terms – has unexpectedly developed a fault. Luckily it broke down right outside a garden centre, so we've been enjoying a campacinno and a coconut pyramid whilst waiting for the AA to arrive.

Ken's initial reaction to the breakdown beggars belief. He clambered on to the roof and began shooting action footage of me pushing the vehicle into the car park. Would you credit it? Fearing his Cuban heels might dent my roof and add to the repair bill, I wrestled Ken to the ground – but I did not, as he claims, do a Chinese burn on his ankles – I was merely trying to get a proper purchase.

Ken's next act of madness was to commandeer one of the garden centre's Hansel and Gretel chalets for use as a makeshift office. He's in there now telephoning Bakewell Library (on his mobile phone) to warn them we're going to be late for the sound check. In fact, he must have finished the call because he's actually beckoning me over. Excuse me, readers.

'Yes, Ken, what is it?'

'John, I've been thinking.'

'What, Ken?'

'We've been setting our sights too low.'

'What do you mean?'

'You're too big for Bakewell Library, John.'

'You've lost the booking, haven't you, Ken?'

'Oh, no, John, but there is a small problem.'

'What's that, then?'

'You'll have to play very quietly – because it's a library, you see. It's something we overlooked, isn't it?'

'Ooph, it is, yes, Ken.'

'Mmm – I mean, do you really want everyone going "shush" when you start singing?'

'No, I want them to be punching the air.'

'And so they shall be, John. I have an alternative venue in mind.'

500 Bus Stops

'Where, Ken?'

'Norway.'

Of course, readers – Norway – the country to whom I once offered my finest song to date 'Pigeons in Flight', in the hope that this would prevent them from getting the usual 'nul points' in the Eurovision Song Contest (although they've been doing much better recently, I notice). But for reasons best known to themselves they decided not to take me up on my kind offer. Whilst most people would have felt very hurt by that and avoided all future dealings with Norway, I decided to turn the other cheek, and give them another chance – should it ever come along.

Well, it did. Shortly after the Eurovision let-down, I spotted a 'Win a Skiing Trip to Norway' competition entry form on the cheese counter at Tesco's. Retiring to the quiet of the wine and spirits section I filled it in there and then. I don't wish to brag, readers, but my slogan had all the credentials to be an outright winner. How heartbreaking, then, to receive only a consolation prize – and not a very nice one at that. I'm not a bad loser, but something wasn't quite right, and I really couldn't let the matter rest there –

17th March, 1992

Dear Graham Weaver,

Thank you for the Jarlsberg shopping bag which I received recently as a runner-up prize in the Tesco's Jarlsberg Cheese Competition.

From the uptone of your accompanying letter I guess you thought I'd be delighted but I'm afraid I can't be, Graham, for two reasons.

First, although it is made of sturdy canvas and has a modern zip fastener, the bag is just too brightly coloured and dainty-looking for a grown man to carry in public. It is also too round and cheesy-looking to be really user-friendly. I'm sorry, but you must have received other complaints about this.

The second reason, Graham, is that I honestly thought I'd done enough to win the first prize of a skiing holiday in Norway. Before you think 'Oo what a big head!', let me say that I wasn't that confident myself until I showed my entry to several people, including a professional agent called Ken Worthington, who you might have heard of. They all said my answer to the tie-breaker was really clever and would probably win first prize. By the way it was 'JARLSBERG IS EXCELLENT FOR COOKING BECAUSE – IT'S THE PURE WAY TO A TASTE OF NORWAY'. I still feel it's very strong and would work well sung or just vocalized over a soft synth backing track. But I guess it's too late now.

What was the winner, by the way? It wasn't by any chance 'TO MAKE YOUR DAY – BAKE NORWAY' was it, because that's the line I came up with first before I rejected it as I thought it was too hard-hitting. If it's that I'll kick myself. Please write back and put me out of my misery, because my wife and I are in agonies knowing that we could have gone to Norway, but somehow it all just slipped away from us.

Thanks again for the shopping bag, Graham. Bye for now.

Kind regards,

John Shuttleworth

Oo – er – I'm suddenly getting cold feet about this Scandinavian jaunt. It's all just a bit sudden, you know. To be honest, I'd be more than happy to dally here in the garden centre while my car's being repaired. An elderly couple have just walked past with a four-foot section of trellis providing me with a lovely whiff of nut-brown wood preservative. I can feel a song coming on. If you don't mind, readers, I'm going to have a little wander.

In the garden centre I could live
Beyond the patio I'd never need to go
For everything this Earth has got to give
To help me through the day is on display
I'd make my bed in a feather-edged shed
And I'd never get fed
Up or down

By the village pump I would contemplate
Never get irate or glum
And by the village pump I would sit and wait
For the other villagers to come
In the garden centre what a happy soul I'd become

I've not told Mary yet about the change of plan. She might be cross at not being invited to Norway, because she'd set her heart on that skiing trip, you know. In fact, we'd both begun a course at our local dry-ski centre – though, to be honest, we weren't very good. Mary kept falling over, and I couldn't stop swerving to the left for some reason. I suppose it's quite funny now looking back, but at the time we weren't laughing.

Then again, I'm glad in a way Mary's not coming. Between you and me she's been a bit moody of late. She wasn't very co-operative when earlier today I wanted a shot of our duvet for the TV Rockumentary, the video Ken's making of our tour, and she gave Ken a nasty shove as we were departing. Quite unnecessary. Mind you, she's always been a bit tetchy – a fact borne out in the following song:

Mary Mary
When I met you I was wary
You looked just like a fairy
But I could see that you were contrary

Mary Mary
When I met you I was wary
You said my arms were hairy
Now that was unnecessary

It was unnecessary, because, on close analysis, you would see that they're not really very hairy at all. Still, I forgave Mary a long time ago, and, to be honest, she's said far more hurtful things since. But I'm going to miss her, and it's the little things about married life that I'll miss most: having a ginger cream popped into your mouth without first requesting one – things like that. Suddenly, marriage seems not like a sentence, but a precious partnership that should be cherished and nurtured. 'Pigeons in flight – I wanna see you tonight.' I do, Mary, you know, but unfortunately it's not possible.

Good old Ken. He's very kindly agreed to ring the AA on my behalf to find out why we've not yet experienced any satisfaction – and to keep an eye out for the recovery vehicle when it eventually arrives. This will allow me to remain in the lean-to conservatory writing my book. Obviously prospective purchasers may wander in at any moment and request that I vacate my wicker chair so that they can try it out, but I'll try not to let them break my concentration.

Well, I think we've exhausted stardom. I'm sure I'll be coming back to it as the tour progresses – especially if stardom becomes a reality – but now, if it's all right with you, readers, I'd like to move on to graver matters.

'Water rip-off!' The poor performance of this particular appliance (despite repeated pumpings) got me quite irate and glum, I can tell you!

How to Have a Pleasant Marriage

1. Find a pleasant partner

Definitely, you should do, though the problem is that everyone is pleasant when you first meet them, aren't they? It's only when you marry them that they turn nasty. Margaret, my first wife, she didn't, but perhaps that's because she didn't have time to – dying as she did a mere three weeks after the wedding. She was stung by a bee, you know, whilst we were gathering blackberries at Wyming Brook. She reacted badly to it – well, anyone would, I suppose – but, no, you know what I mean. She fell into a coma and never regained consciousness. I don't want to talk about it, if that's all right with you. It was a long time ago now, and, although I've never forgiven that particular bee, my anger is lessened when I remind myself that it, too, almost certainly died as a result of the incident (because the stingers come out with bees, don't they, whereas with jaspers they don't).

Time must have softened the blow because recently I even managed to write a song in praise of the bee:

> *Go down on your knee to the honey bee*
> *For she is very nice*
> *Before you kill her with a rolled up* Mirror
> *Think twice*
> *How will that bee's mother feel*
> *When she finds out her child is a ghost?*
> *Kill the bee and ultimately*
> *You'll have nothing to spread on your toast*

There's a second verse, but it's not really good enough to be published, unfortunately.

After Margaret's death I had a death wish, obviously. I used to ride down Ringinglow Road on my Honda 70 at breakneck speed. My visor would be rattling and the buckles on my tartan pannier bags would be ringing shrilly – like a death knell. Sure enough, eventually I came off the machine. But not at speed. No, readers, travelling at approximately six m.p.h., I collided with a pillarbox in Mushroom Lane. It was my own fault. I was steering with one hand. The other hand wasn't available, as it was carrying a packet of crumpets. Crazy, when you consider I had two empty pannier bags crying out to be occupied. I broke my ankle, and ended up in King Edward VII Hospital in Rivelin.

My mother brought me Henry VIII to assemble – you know, the Airfix kit. Because of my black mood I painted it in unorthodox colours – purple all over, if I remember rightly, with a fawn face. That raised some eyebrows in the all-male ward, I can tell you!

During my short stay I played a wicked prank on an ancillary worker named Olive. Olive was deaf, and, one day, as she was hoovering, I pulled out the plug, knowing full well that she'd carry on regardless. Sure enough, she did, right through into the next ward. Well, everybody had a right laugh at this, including a vicar who'd broken his neck playing rugby. I thought he'd have wagged his finger at me and looked all stern, but, no, far from it, and I was a bit of a hero for a time. However, when matron found out who the culprit was she pulled the curtain round my bed, sat down and had a long talk with me, because it was a dirty trick to play, and I fully realize that now.

I had to buy Olive a present, and, after due consideration, I plumped for a quarter pound box of Milk Tray. They don't do that size any more, which is a shame, because it was a nice cheap way to say you were sorry.

In the bed next to me was this bloke called Len who was dying of throat cancer. His daughter, Mary, used to come every night to visit him, and, as his chair was a bit wobbly, used to borrow mine, because I didn't get many visitors, you see. Well, my parents lived over eight miles away in Bamford, and it was awkward for my sister Christine to visit because she emigrated to Canada when she was eighteen with her fiancé, Mark.

A recent snapshot of Mary. (Sorry readers, but when I told her I needed some shots of her for this book she hid all the family photo albums!)

One day Mary came and sat down on my chair without moving it first. She told me her father had gone into a coma so she might as well talk to me that day. After some initial resistance, she agreed to let me read his *Exchange and Mart* – well, he didn't need it any more – and I picked out a little car for her to drive. A blue Hillman Imp, if I recall rightly. She hadn't passed her test, and there was a mutual understanding that the car would never be legally owned by Mary. It was really just part of an elaborate courtship ritual. You know, we were spooning, in the only way we knew how.

Mary's mother had died only a few months previously, so when her father passed away it was nice because in the 'Deaths' column they were able to put: 'A lady passed this way, and a gentleman followed.' I've always liked that one. Very poetical.

Me and Mary began walking out together. I discovered we shared a passion for table tennis, and before long we had commenced weekly training at the local YMCA.

2. Do nice things together

It doesn't have to be ping-pong – though personally I can't conceive of a finer way for husband and wife to unwind together at the end of a hard day. For starters, there's all the hilarity involved in fishing for the ball when it's become stuck beneath the stacking chairs; there's the shaking hands at the end – real physical contact – and, of course, there's the game itself.

Mary always had the sponge bat, and she'd be attacking. I had the hard bat and would be defensive – well back from the table. That's ying and yang or something, isn't it? Somebody told me it was. We used to have these really long rallies – so long sometimes that the little lads on their way to judo class would stop clouting each other with their kitbags and stand and watch us open-mouthed. Ray Pashley, the coach, would wink as he walked past and say 'Another long rally there I see, John'. That made me feel special because he represented South Yorkshire once, you know, when somebody was ill.

Mary doesn't seem to want to play these days, which is a shame – though, to be fair to her, the rubber surface of her bat has become severely perished which could affect her looping shots, and prejudice the final result. I still play on a weekly basis at the drop-in centre, but it's not the same.

Once I had the misfortune to play against Ken Worthington – in a guesthouse in Giggleswick, North Yorks. Honestly, it was like playing a little kid. He kept putting his hand to his mouth and giggling every time he missed the ball, which, in a small child is amusing behaviour, but in a grown man is sickening to behold. I tried to make light of it because I was on holiday, but I couldn't. I don't know why I got so keyed up. It's not Ken's fault he's rubbish at ping-pong.

Mary and I have been happily married now for twenty years. I'm convinced the reason for our success is that we constantly do interesting things together. I help Mary do the weekly shopping, you see. We go to Asda or Morrison's, or, if it's a really big shop, Netto's. I carry the heavier articles such as breakfast cereals, big box powders etc. It's teamwork, isn't it, marriage, and blokes who sit watching Eurosport all day are missing out. Come on, lads, wise up! It's the nineties – time to become a modern man like me.

I'm a modern man
I'm a modern man
I do the household chores whenever I can

I'm a modern man
I'm a modern man
I do the washing up
Apart from the frying pan ('cause it's best to leave that to
soak for a while, isn't it?)

Then on Saturday morning I take
An hour or two out of my life
To go shopping with Mary, my wife

Then we might go to the arcade for a campacinno. That's the new one, isn't it? Yes, it is a little more pricey than the instant, but so lovely and frothy – with its sprinkling of chocolate droppings – that, in my view, it's well worth the extra coppers. But I would advise readers to steer clear of the one you get in a tiny cup with no milk. I'm not sure what it's called, but it's a right rip-off.

Then we might go and get a key cut – you see, you can do things like that when you're in a couple. Yes, you can do it on your own, too, but it's not half as much fun. Because while you're waiting for your key to be cut, you can pop next door and check out holdall prices.

3. Tease your partner with surprise treats

Once you've returned home and unpacked your bags, why not suggest a leisurely drive to the Plague Village of Eyam, or go for a special lunch at the garden centre (£2.95, or £5 for two set meals).

If you've already had your dinner – walk it off with a stroll to the local park. There may be a Dixie band playing, with a bouncy castle or a Tae Kwondo display. When we went the other Sunday, this little lass – she could only have been about five – was throwing this big bloke with a beard over her shoulder. Smashing stuff.

I used to like treating Mary to a trip to the caverns in Castleton, but we don't go down them any more because you get white stuff on your cagoule. Nowadays, we prefer to sit in the café and have a filter coffee and a chocolate brownie. Why don't you do that with your spouse, eh? It's brilliant. On your way home you could stop off at the reservoir to check the level, and have a chat with the ice-cream man – if he's there. He's not always there, of course. But take care as you come up the bank, readers. The other day I lost my footing and fell. But I fell well – you know, I did an RAF roll. Mind you, there's now a small grass stain on my trousers that simply won't go away – despite repeated washings.

'What a ping-pong!' (Ken has suggested that in order to get this shot the ball was glued to my chin. I see what he means, but it wasn't readers, I do assure you.)

Arctic Rock 'n' Roll

4. Develop your own interests

Sometimes circumstances force you and your partner to be apart – trips to Norway, for instance! The enforced separation can put a tremendous strain on the relationship, but it really doesn't need to.

Mary goes to stepclass on a Tuesday night with Joan Chitty, but do I sit around twiddling my thumbs? Not on your nelly! Firstly, I close all the curtains around the house, tucking the hems behind the radiators where applicable. Then I check that the radiator is emitting an even heat throughout its length. If it isn't, I bleed it with an Allen key. If the room is occupied at the time, and the occupant isn't too happy about my presence, I will liaise with them to arrange a more convenient time to return with the Allen key.

On Thursday night when Mary goes to Bums, Tums and Thighs with Doreen Melody, I might go into the garage and write a song or two. If I'm not feeling very creative that night I'll switch off my organ and go and have a little lie-down with a hot milky drink. Alternatively, I'll stand on the landing with the milky drink and listen out for any characteristic knocking noises which would indicate an airlock in the central heating system. (If the house has any serious structural problems, such as subsidence, landslip or heave, this is a perfect opportunity to detect them.)

I'm sure Mary would agree that these periods of enforced separation add sparkle to our relationship, and keep the love-light burning merrily.

5. Don't annoy your partner unduly

It's extremely difficult to predict when the person you are closest to – and know everything about – will suddenly fly into a rage. With Mary, it's impossible. A few weeks ago we did a big shop at Netto's. I was there to carry the heavier items – as you know – and to hold the bags steady as Mary placed the separate items in them.

Readers, please don't think that's all I do at this stage. I'm there in a supervisory capacity, too: checking for splits in the bags, rejecting any that show signs of doing so, and ensuring items aren't too bulky or heavy for their allotted bag. Sometimes I have to be firm and reject a particular product, and this can cause tension between us. Also, because both our heads are bobbing about a bit – Mary's because she's transferring the items from the checkout to the bags, and mine because I'm monitoring the work in progress (which requires a good eyeline at all times) – there's a very real danger of our heads colliding.

Unfortunately, that is exactly what happened on this occasion. On reflection, my big mistake was to chuckle at the incident. But I honestly thought Mary would as well, because it was only a slight contact, you know. Nothing serious. But she didn't chuckle. She went very quiet and handed the money over to the cashier without bothering to first establish eye contact. I, on the other hand, was screwing my face up and going 'Oo!' whilst rubbing my head – to indicate what had happened – before breaking into a reassuring smile, so the cashier would realize it wasn't serious, and that there was no need to press her button for assistance. She still did, though, which was kind of her.

When we got into the car park Mary thumped me really hard on the arm and started shouting – turning the air blue with a torrent of personal abuse. I couldn't believe it. Quite unnecessary.

6. Don't eat your wife's tea

Barry McMahon, who is a painter and decorator, keeps doing stupid things and annoying his wife, Patricia McMahon, who's a good friend of Mary's. You might know her actually because she's a market trader (she sells torches, gaffer tape, that sort of thing). Like Mary, she often wears leggings, but, in Patricia's case, she tucks them into her suede boots, whereas Mary wears sling-backs which her leggings don't quite meet. During the winter months, Patricia sports an anorak with a big hood – the trim of which is made of very fine rabbit fur. It's so fine you can see the path of the wind as it ripples through it (like swaying corn, though on a much smaller scale, obviously). I study her, you see, from the other

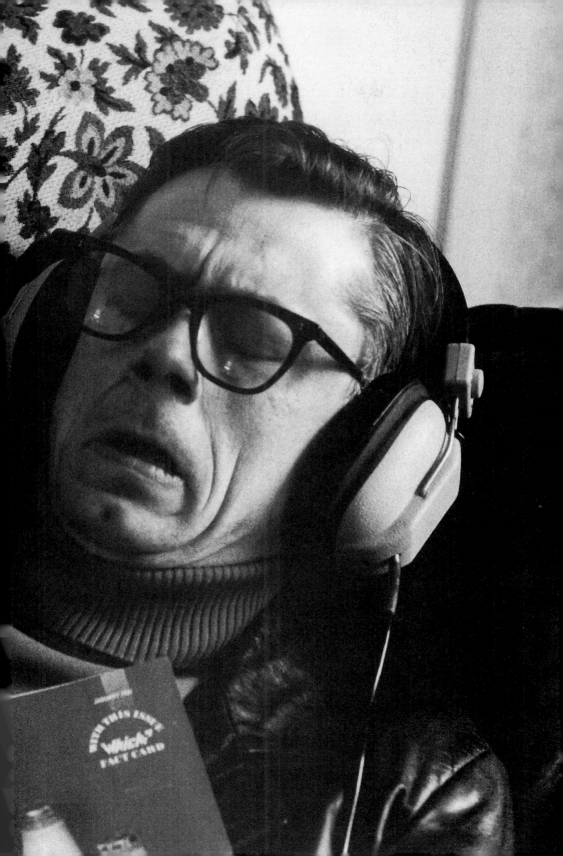

side of the market by the honey stall. I'm there talking to Derek, the stallholder. He's a bit different from the other traders, it must be said, preferring to sit quietly reading a book in between customers. You know, he doesn't call out to advertise his wares. Mind you, that would sound a bit funny, wouldn't it? If Derek started shouting 'Honey, honey!' he'd get some pretty strange looks, I can tell you!

Well, the other night apparently, Barry and Patricia had just sat down to have their tea when the phone rang. It was Patricia's mother in Ripon. (Long-distance call – thought she'd better take it.) So Patricia went to the lounge leaving Barry in the kitchen to eat his tea alone. (That's an unpleasant experience in itself, of course. See 'Dining alone', page 70.)

Well, Barry finished his tea, but Patricia still hadn't returned. So – can you guess what happened next? No? Well, I'll tell you. He started on hers. He did. And when Patricia finally returned upon completion of the call, she found her tea had all been eaten up by Barry. She flew into a rage saying 'What the hell did you do that for? I wanted that!' Barry said 'I don't know, love. I've no explanation,' (or something like that) 'but I'll go to the Chinese and get you a takeout', which is exactly what he did.

However, when Barry returned with the takeaway Patricia was still so angry that she couldn't eat it. So, that's right, you've guessed it – Barry ate it. Then he went upstairs for a little lie-down – well, he was bloated by this stage. Apparently, he lay on his side (in the foetal position, would you believe!), eyes open, looking at the wall, but not answering any of Patricia's questions. And he's still not talking to her. There's no dialogue between the couple, which is very worrying for all concerned.

What's your verdict on that story, readers? Barry's been out of order, don't you think? He needs to get down to the off-licence and buy a box of Moonlight for Patricia pretty sharpish.

What a thoughtful agent Ken Worthington is. Not only has he overseen the removal of my stricken car to a Sheffield garage, but he's also arranged for a luxury tour bus to convey the entire entourage (me and

Ken) to our destination. Fantastic. There'll be a toilet, a snack machine, a video – perhaps even a special writing desk with a drawer full of fancy paper. Things are looking up, and I'll have to go in a minute, readers, to wash my face. But, as Ken's just started tidying his bumbag, perhaps there'll be time to finish this section. There's only one more bit of advice anyway, and it's well worth heeding because, in my experience, it's the only one that seems to work.

7. The case for compromise

I didn't have to relocate my organ in the garage. I could have kept it in the lounge and employed headphone mode, whispering the lyrics to my songs. The risk of saliva dripping on to my slacks could have been minimized by placing a piece of gauze across my lap. But, in the end I moved to the garage because I knew if I didn't Mary might have left me, and I would have been devastated.

Once Mary went to visit her Aunty Janet in South Shields because she was close to death. During Mary's absence, I had to supervise the children which wasn't easy as Karen was a bit wayward at the time. One afternoon she zoomed off to the arcade on her rollerskates. Concerned that pursuing her in my car would endanger my daughter's life – as well as the lives of any pedestrians that might be in the way – I decided to give chase on foot. I only had my slip-ons on, which – without wishing to knock them, you know, they're lovely shoes – couldn't possibly supply the necessary grip required for prolonged bouts of sprinting.

When I finally got Karen back home the house was very untidy, and Darren had prepared a horrible meal. It was an awful period in my life and I was overjoyed when Mary returned with the tragic news that Janet had died at last.

Arctic Rock 'n' Roll

The curious thing is that something good did come out of the fiasco – the following number:

Mary I am missing you
Missing you, missing you
Wishing to be kissing you
But unfortunately I can't

Mary I am missing you
Missing you, missing you
Wishing to be kissing you
But you're visiting a poorly aunt

Do you like that lyric, readers? Ken says it's rubbish, but the point is I know some people who love that song – some friends of ours, Mr and Mrs Whitticar. She's a lab technician. I'm not sure what he does. So it's just a question of taste really, isn't it?

Oops, got to close now, the tour bus has arrived, so I'll catch up with you later, readers!

Hello, it's me again. You won't believe this, but there was no luxury tour bus. It was a wicked prank of Ken's to get me to abandon my car. We're actually on a blinking local service bus. I should have known something was amiss when Ken insisted we wait for it at a bus stop. I feel absolutely gutted.

'Cheer up, John, it might never happen.'

'That's what's worrying me, Ken. You tricked me. We'll never get to Norway by public transport.'

'Get real, John. This is life on the road. It's unpredictable, a wee bit dangerous, yes – but it's rock 'n' roll. At least we're going in the right direction, so settle back and enjoy the ride.'

I'm trying to, readers, but things are going from bad to worse. Not only is this bus not a luxury one – like Ken promised – it's not even going

'Where's the luxury tour bus then?'

in the right direction. I've just spied Chesterfield's legendary crooked spire which means that, instead of going north to Scandinavia, we're heading due south. Now, we'll never get to Norway by nightfall. Or will we? Ken has shrewdly pointed out that it'll still be light whatever time we get there because in Norway during the summer months it's perpetual daylight. It's a fair point, but, to be honest, I'm beginning to lose heart. Perhaps Norway was a bit ambitious – by bus anyway. I reckon we should try again tomorrow when my car's been fixed.

Lady luck is definitely not on our side today, readers. We'd just spotted a branch of Iceland, the frozen food store which – as Ken pointed out – would have been an even better venue than Norway (just as impressive on my CV and more convenient), but would you blinking well credit it? We were so astounded at our good fortune that we forgot to get off the bus, and we are now bound for Matlock, which claims to have a Spa – though I've never seen one.

'Have you, Ken?'

'Come to think of it, no, I haven't John. It's got a Londis, I know that – '

'Mm – it's very distressing, not least because I know somebody who lives in Chesterfield who might have come along and offered his support.'

'Who's that then, John?'

'Ray – erm – somebody. He runs a sports shop.'

'Does he now, John?'

'He does, and his son, Eamonn, who's a police cadet, recently won a personality competition. I mean, he just had to announce his name and hobbies into a microphone at a local disco. But he had to keep dancing while he did it – you know, it can't have been that easy.'

It's a shame about Iceland because it would've been full of chest freezers – the surface I'm most comfortable performing on. But fret ye not, readers. Upon alighting from the bus at Matlock what should we spy on the other side of the road but a blinking freezer shop! It was too

500 Bus Stops

good an opportunity to miss, and Style 72 on my Yamaha soon had the customers rocking in the aisles. (Incidentally, in lieu of payment, the manager gave us a damaged pack of mini Yorkshire puddings to take with us to the guesthouse – a fantastic gesture!)

Am I upset that we didn't make it to Norway? Not really, readers, because there's something that in the excitement I'd forgotten – they kill whales, don't they, Norway, and they really shouldn't. I suppose coming last in the Eurovision Song Contest so often with 'nul points' made them very bitter, and so they started looking for a scapegoat. Being so big, whales were an obvious target. (Perhaps also their habit of continually blowing out water might be misconstrued as a mocking gesture – you know, like they're blowing a raspberry at Norway and really rubbing it in that they're not very good at songwriting.)

If this is the case, I reckon Norway are missing the point, i.e. they shouldn't be attacking marine life – they should be harpooning the songwriters, really, shouldn't they!

Save the whale
Its fins, its hump, its tail
Stop the slaughter, don't you think you ought ter
Save the whale?

We don't have to kill the whale
To have a lovely time
There are lots of other fish
Upon which we can dine
Pilchards in tomato sauce –
An old favourite of mine
And tuna chunks in brine
And tuna chunks in brine

Don't be naughty, Norway
To kill the whale's a crime
There are lots of other fish
Upon which you can dine
Have you tried a cod portion
In parsley sauce – divine!
And tuna chunks in brine
And tuna chunks in brine.

(Everybody!)

Save the whale
Its fins, its hump, its tail
Stop the slaughter
Don't you think we ought to save the whale...

Well, readers, you won't believe what Ken's doing. He's spread out those mini Yorkshire puddings on top of the telly to defrost them and keeps prodding them with his little finger. (Alas, there is no microwave in our hotel bedroom.) What an idiot!

Ken's big mistake was not to do what I did – I got a beef bap and a six-pack of Mint Viscounts from the Jet garage on the other side of the bypass, and I'm laughing now. Well, I'm not laughing, but I'm reasonably contented.

Goodnight, readers.

Here I am – when I had a bit of a quiff – studying the lyrics of 'Good Morning Starshine'. (In my opinion it is excellent, and requires no further honing.)

2

Strangeways

Tips for Diners and How to Find a Real Bargain

Good morning, readers. Firstly, I hope you slept better than I did. Ken Worthington kept me awake by pacing up and down in the hotel room with a beaker of Malibu until the wee small hours. The worst thing was he didn't vary his route – you know, he passed by the side of my bed at exactly the same point on each of his circuits, letting out a huge sigh as he did so.

Then, just when I'd finally managed to drop off, I was promptly woken up again by the sound of a sash window being forced open, and in the half light I could see Ken attempting to lift the TV up on to the windowsill.

'What was that all about, Ken?'

'Oh hallo, John. Yes, well I was going to chuck it out of the window, then tell the manager you'd done it so you'd be thrown out of the hotel.'

'That's not very nice of you, Ken. But tell me, what was your motive?'

'I was merely trying to raise some much needed media interest in the tour, John. Who knows, you might have ended up on *Look North.*'

'Yes, but I wouldn't have been able to watch it, Ken, because I wouldn't have had a telly. As it was, when I arose at 7 a.m., I saw a smashing programme on the history of canals.'

This morning Ken's erratic behaviour has continued. In an American-style diner in Matlock, he began (without warning or the slightest provocation) to lob sachets of demerara sugar at my torso. (I believe he was aiming for the head and neck area, but, fortunately, Ken's a lousy shot.)

In the end, we had to beat a hasty retreat after Ken told the waitress I was leaving without paying my bill. Well, I was, but only because Ken had assured me it was his treat. The lunatic! What the hell was he playing at? I think he wants to mould me into a wild man of Rock, which is fair enough, I suppose. But he mustn't rush me. Moreover, it mustn't be achieved at the expense of good table manners which I've always observed. I'm sure you have, too, readers, but if, like Ken, you've been guilty of slovenly behaviour at the tea table, then please heed carefully the following advice. But, before we get on to 'Tips for Diners', you'll be wondering, no doubt, if there's any news on my car. Unfortunately there isn't (but thanks for your concern). So we're back on the bus – a blinking double-decker actually – which is far too bumpy for writing on.

I'm feeling a bit nauseous, but at least I can work without being interrupted – Ken's fallen asleep you see, which is hardly surprising.

500 Bus Stops

Hmm – I wouldn't mind a nap myself, but someone has to be awake to greet the inspector should he decide to swoop.

Hang about, Ken's stirring – smacking his lips in a comical fashion. Oo… his eyes have just popped open and he's pulling that face he pulled when he was on *New Faces* in '73 – the one that looks like he's just seen a ghost.

'Have you just seen a ghost, Ken?'

'Pardon? Where are we, John?'

'On the outskirts of Buxton, Ken. But more importantly, where are we heading, because you've not told me today's itinerary?'

'Well, John, I think you're ready now for a larger arena. And with it being summertime, I thought you wouldn't mind playing outdoors.'

'Oo! Right, Ken! As long as it's not too late. I'd be delighted. Someone's having a barbecue, are they? No? A nurses' garden party?'

'Think bigger, John.'

'Oo, I see! An agricultural show!'

'No, but there may be animals present.'

'I give in, Ken. Tell me, where.'

'A rock festival, John!'

'What, like Donington, *Monsters of Rock*?'

'Yes, John, something like that.'

'But, Ken, there'll be bare ladies present, won't there? And access to the love-drug – E? I'm not doing it, Ken.'

'But, John, it's an ideal opportunity to tap the lucrative youth market.'

'Is it, Ken?'

'Yes, and you'll find them more than willing to punch the air with you. No one'll be wandering back to their rooms.'

'Oh, go on then, Ken, I'll give it a whirl.'

Well, readers, that's something to look forward to, isn't it? But first things first. It's time for me to give you some more sound advice. (Luckily, Ken's dozed off again so we should be able to crack on without any distractions.)

Tips for Diners

I once attended a conference in Barnsley for Security Personnel. During the lunch break I went to the canteen with my voucher and – unable to find a table for one – joined a Rentokil rep from Thirsk. We'd established eye contact briefly when one of my Opal Fruits went flying during the opening address. He kindly pointed out its eventual resting place – under the runner of a stacking chair three rows away. (Incidentally, although badly misshapen, it was still highly edible.)

He was slight of build, this chap, well-groomed with a neat tidy beard, and naturally he'd already made a good impression on me. However, as I reached for the salt and pepper the tops came off in my hand, spilling the cellars' contents over the table. Though slightly dubious, I immediately ruled him out as the culprit (because of his smart appearance and the responsible behaviour he'd displayed earlier). So, instead of saying 'Hey! What the hell did you do that for?', I went to inform the supervisor that a prankster was in the building – picking up a dishcloth en route and a sachet of tartar sauce for my Scotch egg. Upon my return I cleaned up the mess and then sat down to eat my dinner.

Something wasn't quite right about my meal, though for a while I couldn't identify the problem. Suddenly I twigged – my lettuce was missing. I looked at this chap and he was sniggering to himself. Then, before my very eyes, he slowly raised his hands revealing a lettuce leaf in each of his palms. In a very calm voice he said 'Is this what you've been looking for?' I was utterly flummoxed. I just didn't know what to do. Well, would you? It's something no one could ever prepare for, is it – a grown man in a nice suit nicking your lettuce. What the hell was going on? I don't know and still don't to this day.

I couldn't let him get away with it though, so I took the slice of lemon from my prawn cocktail and dropped it into his glass of water. That'll teach him to play silly buggers, I thought. But, in my angry state, I'd completely forgotten something. Nowadays a slice of lemon's quite a desirable thing to have in your water, isn't it? So, of course, he said

500 Bus Stops

'Thanks very much, my friend. Much obliged to you', although he was definitely shaking a bit. You know, the message had got through that I wasn't going to be mucked about any more.

Where's your manners?

What I've just described is an extreme example of misbehaviour at the dining table. Most other instances are of a more minor nature, and may go undetected by fellow diners. You, yourself, might not even be aware of your rude behaviour. But be assured that humming, talking with your mouth full, leaning back on your chair, and swinging your legs rhythmically – whether you're making contact with the table leg or not – are all unacceptable. You mustn't do any of those things because, you know, it's very naughty.

It's sometimes tricky to gauge the right thing to say to the person who's made the meal. If you don't compliment them enough they're liable to get grumpy and say 'Don't you like it, then?' On the other hand, if you overdo it – showering the chef with constant praise – they're liable to say 'Just shut up and eat your dinner!' So you can't win really, can you? But don't despair. I've discovered the exact number of compliments required to please the cook – three. That's right, three.

The first compliment should be given as you sit down – 'Oo, this looks lovely' is what you say. The second – delivered after a couple of mouthfuls – is 'Mm – this is lovely – ' with emphasis on the word 'is'. Say nothing then until the very end of the meal, then, as you get down, say, 'Mmm – that was really lovely. Thank you.' This phrase should ideally coincide with both hands patting the tummy. (Sounds like it could be tricky, doesn't it, readers – like rubbing your head at the same time as patting your tummy. But relax. What I'm talking about is not quite the same thing.)

If you wish to reinforce your gratitude with an offer to wash up that's entirely a matter for you and your conscience. It really depends on what's on telly at that point, doesn't it? I enjoy washing up, myself –

especially at night. I like seeing all the reflections on the shiny plates, and plunging my hands into piping hot water – safe in the knowledge that my fleecy rubber gloves will prevent them from being scalded.

Dining alone

To be honest, I don't like eating alone. Yes, there is a certain kudos in sitting high up on a stool at the breakfast bar with a soft drink, a plateful of assorted sandwiches and Ken Bruce cracking jokes in the background. But where are you supposed to look whilst chewing, eh, that's what I'd like to know? These clever-clog scientists seem to have an answer for all Man's problems, but they haven't solved that one yet, have they?

When you're dining with others there's no problem. You can observe their cheek movements as they chew, or – if they're getting well stuck in like my son Darren tends to – study the top of their head. Or you can just look at their plates and gauge how much is left on them compared to your own, and even speculate as to which bits (if any) will remain uneaten.

When I'm eating on my own, my eyes go all over the place in a desperate search for a focal point. Honestly, it makes me feel quite giddy, and can even cause loss of appetite.

At the garden centre I'm generally at a table for one, but at least there are things to look at and study – the giant fan, for example, and other diners with whom to establish eye contact. But you have to be careful. Sometimes it seems they're looking directly at you with eyes wide open as if they're pleased to see you. Before you give them the thumbs up, make sure they're not merely concentrating on removing a lump of gristle from one of their fillings.

I like to sit near the till. I enjoy hearing its merry ring and observing the ladies going in and out through the saloon-style doors, which I'm also fairly close to. You might be thinking 'why, you fool? Doesn't the fanning effect of the doors continually opening and closing rapidly cool down your meal?' All I can say to that is, no, it doesn't seem to. Indeed,

I'd go further and claim that it actually heats it up because blasts of hot air from the kitchen keep coming my way.

The pleasures of dining out

Sometimes Ken joins me at the garden centre – if he's in the mood for a sit-down meal. Being of a quicksilver disposition he lacks the patience to queue up and then remain in fixed seating for lengthy periods. Ken prefers fast food eaten in an upright position.

But on those occasions Ken chooses to dine with me, we have a smashing time studying the menu to see what we might have ordered if we hadn't chosen what we did choose, comparing napkins and cutlery (they're always the same), and, if there's time, discussing my future in the entertainment business.

We walk off our dinner with a leisurely stroll past the pot animals to the village pump. If the weather's fine we may venture beyond the bronze buddhas (£6.95) to the sheds' section where Ken always insists upon entering the Hansel and Gretel chalet, even though he knows he shouldn't because it's for children really. (Nevertheless, a grown man can stand fully erect inside one – they've an apex roof, you see.)

One of the delights of shopping with Mary is stopping at the café in the arcade for a campacinno. If it's busy and there are no tables free it doesn't worry us in the slightest. We're quite happy standing with our coffees placed on the narrow bar that runs around the café perimeter. I particularly enjoy holding on to the chrome upright and peering under the rail to see if there are any youths running amok by the fountain. After a while, Mary always tells me to let go of it, but, I have to say she's being a fool, because surely that's what it's there for.

Emerging from a Hansel and Gretel chalet. (Despite the apex roof, I deemed it judicious to stoop slightly.)

The perils of dining out

....

A young business couple who Ken knows once had a bad experience at a restaurant. Both members of the couple are in full employment and they have no offspring, which could explain why they're quite well off. Indeed, I've learnt from Ken that last Bonfire Night they spent the incredible sum of £180 on fireworks – including £30 on a pyramid. But, listen to this, you had to be seventy-five feet away from the pyramid, and they've only got a little patio, so they had to view it from a few gardens away. Unfortunately their eyeline wasn't very good – a dense buddleia bush (so favoured by butterflies during the summer months) was in the way, so, of course, they missed it. Mind you, I reckon it serves them right for being so swanky.

That's by the by. One night, they went for a meal at a posh Italian restaurant that had just opened. (Mind you, it can't be that posh because they've got a blackboard for the menu – just like in a fishmonger's. I can't believe it.)

Anyhow, they were given a table right next to this blackboard, and she was having difficulty in viewing it because his head was in the way. (He's got hair like Art Garfunkel, you see, it's quite thick and springy.) Well, she was saying 'Shift, I can't see!' and he was dodging and weaving but she still couldn't see properly, and they were both getting quite irate. To be fair, she needed to view the menu in its entirety in order to make an informed choice, but, with him in the way, it was never going to be possible. Eventually she smacked him one – not hard, but it was enough for him to get up and leave the restaurant in a huff. He'd had enough, and understandably so.

Apparently he went straight to the all-night garage and bought a burger, eating it whilst chatting to the proprietor (I hope he didn't speak with his mouth full!). This bloke had just taken over the franchise and was having a few teething problems, you see. Meanwhile, the wife had

Strangeways

remained in the restaurant determined to make her selection, and, of course, she was now free to do that. Or was she? The cruel irony is that, now she was a lone diner, she was moved to a table for one right next to the kitchen where her view of the menu was even worse than before. So she just sat all night drinking champagne, and eating them little breadsticks they give you when you first come in. An awful tale, I'm sure you'll agree, and one that they will have to carry with them to their respective graves.

Eat at a reasonable hour

At home we have our tea at fiveish. Any later and Mary's too bloated to do her step class. I, too, would not be in good shape to tackle the evening's DIY tasks until at least eight o'clock, and that's no time to be mounting creaky stepladders, is it? I have to consider the man across the road who's just come out of hospital, and by that time all the babies are sleeping, remember.

Having said that, if, say, I've seriously overestimated the amount of Polyfilla required for filling a crack in a skirting board, I might find myself pacing round the house for ages in search of further cracks in which to deposit the remaining Polyfilla. On one occasion – it was after eleven – Mary was hissing at me to come to bed, but I still had a bit of Polyfilla left on my saucer. (It had gone quite hard by this time, of course, though repeated deposits of spittle had kept it just about workable.) In a desperate attempt to finish it all up, I started doing a neighbour's wall – in complete darkness, I couldn't see a blinking thing!

Young people don't eat at a reasonable hour, though, do they. I know they don't because there's a group of them living opposite me in the big house that's a bit dilapidated. I usually take Kirsty for a walk at about eight o'clock – 8.05 – something like that. We'll have had our tea and washed up hours ago, but those young people will be just sitting down to a big meal, with candles and everything. And this is mid-week, you

'Poly put the filla on!'

know. Honestly, it's like Santa's grotto, and they have no net curtains up, so you can see everything.

I return from my walk at about nine o'clock – 8.57 – somewhere in that region. Now, they'll have finished their tea, but they won't have got down. They'll still be sat at the table drinking coffee and playing with bits of paper. Funny, isn't it?

I don't want to be nasty, but those young people get on my nerves, and I'll tell you why. My brother-in-law, Carl, paid us a visit recently in his new car. It's a Proton – J reg. A fantastic motor. We thought it would be nice to have a photo of him sat in it in front of our house next to my Austin Ambassador. (There's plenty of room because we've had it concreted over now at the front – it looks much smarter.)

Then Darren's friend Plonker arrived. He's called Lee really, but he prefers it if you call him Plonker. He says 'Call me Plonker, Mr Shuttleworth. Everyone does, you know'. So you do and, yes, at first you feel a bit awkward. But, after a while, it becomes easy and you find yourself saying 'Come here, Plonker,' without the slightest hesitation. Anyway, Plonker's got a maroon Datsun which, after much manoeuvring, was parked up next to my vehicle.

At this point Ken appeared and expressed an interest in placing his Honda Civic next to Carl's Proton. It was a lovely idea, but, after much soul-searching, I had to say 'Sorry, Ken, there's no room'. Because there wasn't, you know. As you can imagine, he didn't like that at all!

Mary then duly arrived with the camera. After much coaxing (from yours truly) she stood on the garden wall and prepared to take a photo of us all sat in our respective vehicles. As she said 'Cheese!' I spotted a very sad sight. Ken was sat in his drive behind the wheel of his car grinning along with the rest of us. (He had clearly not given up hope of being in the photo – but it was a pipe-dream, and Ken must have known that. He was out of the shot – cut off completely.)

Then when Mary had taken the photo, I glanced across the road and saw all those young people stood in their bay window killing themselves laughing. I really don't know why because they haven't got a vehicle between them!

I would like to end this mouth-watering section, with the story of the time I took Mary for a meal at a carvery in the Plague Village of Eyam. Ken tagged along, and we got a taxi there and back because we were having a drink, you know. Indeed, you may be interested to learn that our return taxi fare came to £16.90, which is a hell of a sum – more than the meal itself, for all three of us.

'Camp'acinnoing it up at the splendid Eyam tearooms.

I'd have preferred the meter to have stopped on £16.65, partly for the obvious reason that I'd have been 25p better off, but also because 1665 was the year of the Plague, wasn't it – the year the tailor brought the offending bundle of cloth to Eyam. But I was crazy to have wanted that, wasn't I? Think about it readers... Well, it's increments of ten on the meter, isn't it!

Since that night, whenever I've driven to Chatsworth Park for an ice-cream, I've always made a detour to Eyam so that I can fill up at the local garage with, yes – you've guessed it, £16.65 worth of petrol. The lad on the till doesn't seem to understand the significance of what I'm doing. (To be fair to him, perhaps he's from a neighbouring village that was untouched by the appalling tragedy – and it was quite a long time ago now, I suppose.)

Back to our marvellous night out in Eyam. Ken displayed extremely bad manners by overloading his plate with shepherd's pie. Mary was guilty of the opposite vice – the portions she allocated herself were miserly, and she paid the price for this later on in the meal, as you are about to hear in the song I wrote immediately upon our return home. (By the way, readers, when you read the first line you may think it's a well-known nursery rhyme. Don't be fooled – it's not!)

Mary had a little lamb
Green beans and new potatoes
I had tuna and sweetcorn flan
We served ourselves – no waiters
(because it was a carvery you see)

Ken plumped for the shepherd's pie
I said 'Ken, you're outrageous'
For he had piled his plate sky-high
To eat it took him ages

'The perils of dining out!' My mid-morning snack is being disrupted by a *ferocious jasper who is about to alight on my shoulder. Can you spot him?*

We had a carafe of sweet white wine
And Ken had a gin and tonic
There was a giraffe for children to climb
Though no children were on it...

Mary had a little lamb
But that was her big folly
For she was famished when it came
To viewing the sweet trolley
A substantial main course would have made
A sweet unnecessary
As it was she suffered
'Rigor Mortis by Raspberry'!

I could do with some shepherd's pie right now, actually – with a portion of garden peas, and a few button mushrooms, too, if possible. For my sweet, I'd like fruit cocktail and evaporated milk, please. Phwor! It'd be wonderful, and might help to settle my stomach.

Yes, I'm currently experiencing a few tummy problems, readers. It's being constantly on the road that's doing it – grabbing a quick bite here and there at roadside snack bars, bus station cafés, and even eating on the bus itself. I'd advise against that – especially on a bus in the heart of the Peak District. I've just had two mini pork pies, a fun-pack of snack-sized Crunchie bars, a can of lime cordial, and half a tube of Parma Violets, and, to be honest, I feel a bit queasy.

The mystery is that Ken seems to be thriving on a similar diet. Maybe that's because he's used to eating on the move – literally. Oh, yes, back home, I've often spotted Ken scoffing a trayful of chips and curry sauce whilst doing a little tap dance on his lawn. Sometimes he'll disappear behind a bush, only to reappear stepping gingerly along the narrow coping stones of his patio wall. That's crazy, isn't it – to be putting your life in danger while having your dinner. Certainly it can't be good for digestion. To make matters worse, I've reason to believe

500 Bus Stops

Ken is humming as he eats, which is a bit rude really, isn't it?

But Ken is a bit rude, as you know. And throughout the day he's been encouraging me to be the same – suggesting I throw an ice-cream wrapper on the ground in full view of the ice-cream vendor – even though there was a bin a few yards away. I'm also being dissuaded from thanking bus drivers as we alight. Ken has suggested 'Drop dead, daddio' would be a more suitable parting phrase.

I don't see that all this unpleasantness is necessary myself, but Ken assures me it is if I'm going to appeal to the nation's youth, and appear a credible force at tonight's open-air rock festival. However, Ken came a cropper with his most recent stunt.

The plan was doomed to failure, as I'm sure you'll agree when you hear it – which you will do now, because I'm going to tell it you. Yes, the plan was that I should get on the bus and walk past the driver without paying. Ken would be immediately behind filming me as the irate driver opened his little door and chased me down the aisle demanding payment. I would refuse – a scuffle would ensue, and in the end I'd be thrown off the bus for fare dodging.

Ken would have captured the ugly episode on camera, which, once shown to representatives of the local press, would wind up being the cover story of that evening's final edition. My name would be mud, but at least it would be in print, and ticket sales for that night's show would benefit enormously.

But Ken was forgetting something. When two people get on a bus and the first walks straight past the driver in search of a seat, it's automatically assumed by the driver that the second person will be paying for both of them. Which is exactly what Ken had to do. What an idiot, and yet how generous of him to pay not only his own fare, but mine, too!

Naturally, Ken went bright red with embarrassment – so red, in fact that for a time his complexion matched almost exactly the mauve cycling top that he's wearing today. Indeed, if you were being fanciful, readers, you might claim he resembled Professor Plum – you know the little man in Cluedo that you move – except that Ken has an afro, which of course, Professor Plum doesn't have.

What's he like, eh? Well, that's a question Ken asked me himself shortly after the incident. It's a tricky one, that. I thought the best way to answer it was to write a song and perform it for Ken on the bus – whilst Ken operated the puppet we've brought along with us. It's a nice way to represent Ken when his actions are worthy of note (because he can't appear in the Rockumentary, remember) and it's visual stimuli – to keep the viewers' interest up – because I'm a bit boring to look at after a while. I know that, you know.

'Can you ken Ken?' This puppet bears no resemblance whatsoever to the real Ken Worthington (apart from the eyes and nose – and the way his arms are outstretched in a pleading fashion).

You're like a halo – you go above some people's heads
You're like a biro – sometimes you're blue and sometimes red
You're like a Volvo – you keep your lights on in the day
Like a last Rolo – you rarely give yourself away

You're like a Polo – your hole is greater than your parts
But you're not like Eric Bristow – i.e. you're terrible at darts
You're like a peanut – you sometimes end up on the floor
You're like a teacup – you're not a mug, and that's for sure

You're like you, like you
And no other comparison will do
You're like you, like you
Not quite but close enough for you to sue

Can you ken Ken?
Can you ken Ken?
You may be able to cancan
But can you ken Ken?

I've just glanced out of the window and I see that no longer are we amongst picturesque countryside. I do believe we're entering the city of Manchester.

'Ken, why have we come to Manchester?'

'Well, John, Manchester is Sin City, a mecca for leisure, drug-seekers, and a hotbed of fashion and fun.'

'Yet they failed in their bid to host the Olympic games, Ken. It doesn't make sense.'

To be perfectly honest with you, readers, until recently I've never thought much of Manchester. But last year I took Mary to Granadaland and we had a fantastic time. I had my video done talking to Betty Turpin in the Rovers. It was only a tenner, and a fantastic memento for anyone who wants it, you know. We had a lovely day, and Mary looked super in her tracksuit and sunglasses. She also had a new shoulder bag which made a nice noise as it opened – a sort of ripping sound (would that be velcro, then?).

The whole experience left a deep impression on me, and that evening I wrote – 'You're like Manchester' – a frank account of my feelings for my wife and my new regard for this once great cotton town.

You're like Manchester
You've got Strangeways
But you've got Styal too
And I miss you while I'm away

You're as pretty as that city
In autumn too
And you're like Manchester
'Cause I love you

You're like Manchester
You've got Strangeways
You are my queen and like a
Certain town
Will always rain!

You're as pretty as that city
In autumn too
And you're like Manchester
'Cause I love you

But if you're like Manchester
Don't you Cheetam me
If I Rusholme to find you've been in
Whalley's Range I won't be pleased

My Belle Vue of the world
Will become a Fallowfield
But I know I can trust yer
You're like Manchester…

I hope you liked that one, readers, and noted the clever word play.

Well – I'm in a charity shop now searching for items of clothing with which I aim to create a new image for myself. An image that'll make me more palatable to younger rock fans. I was quite happy with my old image myself – smart but casual, you know – but it's the next stage in Ken's all important star-grooming programme, and I want to score high marks so I can move swiftly on to the next one – whatever that might be!

Having said that, I'm sorely tempted to abandon my search for a snazzier look and have a real good browse instead. Now would be a good time because Ken has just nipped out to try and find one of those little booths that do ear piercing. Before any of you say, 'Oh, no, John, don't have your ear pierced. That's taking things too far!', I should tell you that it's not me that's having the operation, it's Ken. (I suppose he's worried that I might get ahead in the fashion stakes and he's going to appear dowdy next to me.)

I understand his concern, but he's no need to worry. Ken's a very natty dresser, and has been since the days he was 'TV's Clarinet Man'. Then he had a Cat Stevens perm, wore a sky-blue shirt with a Slim Jim tie, plus he had the loon pants and the Cuban heels. He had the lot in fact. He still dresses the same way, though his hair has now become a full-blown afro, plus he wears a bumbag and a Whitesnake bomber jacket to bring his image slap-bang into the nineties.

Actually, Ken may be gone some time so perhaps it would be judicious to stop eyeing the wooden donkey in the corner and begin dispensing tips on bargain hunting. Well, why not? You can't deny I'm in the right place to be discussing such matters. Very well, then. I'll just sit myself down in the changing booth, draw the curtain, and then I'll begin.

Perusing the '£500 and under' column. Incredibly, there were four Austin Ambassadors for sale – all X reg, alas!

How to Find a Real Bargain

I anticipate this section will be very popular, because everyone likes a good bargain, don't they? Indeed, it wouldn't surprise me if many of you have flipped straight to this bit without reading the earlier chapters. If so, it's understandable but I do think you're making a grave error, readers. Please be patient. You'll come to this chapter eventually. Now go back to the beginning of the book and learn about how to become famous. Thank you.

To those remaining readers I say 'Nice to have you with me still. We've come quite a long way together already, haven't we', but there's still a heck of a journey, I must stress that.

Now then – bargains. Everyone knows a good bargain when they see one I reckon – it's just knowing where to look for it that causes problems.

Look locally

The *Exchange and Mart* may contain more bargains than the small-ad section of your local paper, but they're usually too far away, aren't they? What is the point of spotting '100 assorted wing-nuts, £1.50', getting all excited, and then realizing you'll have to trek out to North Wales just to view them.

I once made the mistake of driving all the way to Keighley, West Yorks, to check out 'Two Mr Bean videos – £7 each'. I enjoy the hilarious antics of the accident-prone Mr Bean as much as the next person, but, for a second-hand video, £7 seemed dreadfully pricey. That was half the reason I responded to the ad, actually. I was curious to know just exactly what the vendor's game was, to learn a little about their personal history etc., anything that would give me a psychological advantage and help me knock them down to a reasonable sum (£3 each I thought, or £5 for both).

When I finally got there, a lady answered the door with the chilling news that they'd already been sold. Sold! It couldn't be possible. Suddenly those Mr Bean videos seemed the most desirable thing on earth. I asked her if she was absolutely certain they weren't still available, adding that I'd even be prepared to pay the full asking price. She shook her head sadly, but with a big smile on her face as well – which seemed rather suspicious to me.

At this point, it started snowing. Time was running out for me, and I knew it. I said that, as I'd come such a long way, couldn't she at least tell me the circumstances behind the sale? She said it was none of my business, but, if I really wanted to know, the videos were her son's and that he'd been forced to sell them to help fund a school trip to Amsterdam.

Quick as a flash, I enquired whether there were any other items in his bedroom up for grabs – military memorabilia, a small child's karate suit – that sort of thing. At this point, she started to close the door. Well, she had to, to prevent her toddler son from escaping. He'd spotted the snow, you see, and naturally wanted to go out and play in it, like little kiddies do – though he was being a bit premature, I reckon. It had barely begun to settle at this stage.

Radio phone-ins

Not an obvious situation for bargains to be had, but the penny-wise punter would do well to get dialling. The other week my nephew, Dale, rang in to a local radio station to complain about the music they were playing. He said there was too much rap and funkadelia, and that they should be playing more rockabilly. Well – they had him on air for about five minutes, apparently – the DJ asking him all about his wall-papering, and demanding he describe the pattern for the listeners. He even waited while Dale popped up the ladder to stick back a bit that was peeling off. The DJ was saying things like 'Dale, where are you? Come back, we miss you, Dale! Oo, he's coming back now. I can hear the squeak of the ladder' – silly stuff like that. (I missed it, unfortunately, because I had to go to the charity shop to examine a 1000-piece jigsaw that had come in earlier in the week.)

The DJ obviously took a shine to Dale because his name went into a computer draw and he ended up winning five CDs. That's not bad, is it, considering he'd rung up to complain!

There was a problem, though. Dale hadn't got a CD player. (Like me, he's waiting till prices tumble sufficiently.) So he had an idea. He rang up the radio station again and asked to be put through so he could complain to the DJ that he hadn't got a CD player, and then the DJ could say something like 'Not you again', but be laughing while he said it, you know, and then put his name into another draw which he'd win, and the prize would be a CD player.

It was a nice idea, well thought out with a fairytale ending, and the programme's producer was obviously tempted, but they had to get some adverts in before the News – which was extended with *Euro 96* – and then it was the *Folk Show*, and the DJ was an old bloke who didn't think it was very funny. Dale gradually realized it wasn't going to happen for him, so he hung up. But he was philosophical about it. You know, he refused to let it get him down.

A local resident enviously eyes the bargain product I've discovered – but she's too late. It's mine!

Charity shops

I'm in one right now, as you know, and it's frustrating that I've got to be writing my book. I'd rather be examining all the marvellous little items on display, sorting through the bargain bucket for early Nolan Sisters' LPs, that sort of thing.

The great advantage of shopping in charity shops (if it's your local one) is that you will more than likely know one of the ladies behind the counter, so you can enjoy a chin-wag as you bargain hunt. Having said that, after a time, they can get a bit snappy, and say you'll have to excuse them because they're very busy. So you wander off to have one more look at the lemon squeezer – checking for imperfections in the glass and holding it to the sunlight to see if a prism effect can be achieved – but every time you look round they're not busy at all. They're just standing there watching you. If that's being busy I'd hate to catch them during a quiet moment!

I'm going to have to put my pen down now, readers, and try on some eye-catching garments. Ken's back and, in case you're wondering, he hasn't had his ear pierced. He bottled out when they told him he wouldn't be receiving a general anaesthetic, which is fair enough, I reckon. He's on his mobile phone trying to persuade a local journalist that my antisocial behaviour earlier today would make interesting copy, but I don't think he's having much luck. By the sound of things this bloke's laughing his head off, which is riling Ken in a big way. In fact, Ken's gone bright red again. Oh dear.

Well, readers, the transformation is now complete. I've got a brand new image. It's quite radical, I must say, although I have been allowed to hang on to my fawn slacks and my polo neck.

'What do you think, Ken?'

'Here's to the new Me!' (What do you think, readers? Snazzy, eh?)

'You look marvellous, John.'

'I'm not so sure, Ken. I'm getting some funny looks.'

'That's because you look like a star, John. People are trying to work out who you are, so act like a star!'

'It's all very well, Ken, saying "act like a star", but I've still got some important tips on bargain hunting to give you, and I'd rather do that now than later tonight when I'm all tense preparing to face thousands of hysterical youngsters.'

Luckily we're back on the bus heading for the city centre where Ken wants to film me signing autographs, so I'll carry on where I left off, if I may.

What a card!

Next time you pop into your local newsagents for a tube of mints and a paper, don't forget to look at the 'for sale' cards in the window. Some are very drab and to study them for long periods can become boring. But others are extremely eye-catching – with clever swirly writing and even little pictures at the side.

Recently I noticed a card advertising 'Private French lessons'. The teacher obviously had a sense of humour as she'd included a drawing of herself dressed as a maid spanking a naughty pupil. That made me chuckle, and I was quite tempted to make further enquiries because I'm not very good at French, you know, and I'd like to improve. Pupils were promised warm, pleasant surroundings, which makes sense (you can't be writing those awkward little accents with frozen fingers now, can you?) and discretion was assured – another nice touch. Well, the last thing you want is the teacher telling everyone that your accent's terrible.

Occasionally, cards are placed in the window that contain misleading information. What appears to be a great offer may be an attempt to hurt or embarrass a respectable member of the community. Barry McMahon – you know, the painter and decorator who so naughtily ate his wife's tea – was recently the victim of such a prank. Barry had been contracted to

500 Bus Stops

creosote the shed of a partially disabled man called Brian. A friendship developed between the two men, but it began to deteriorate almost immediately after rumours were circulated by Brian about Barry not cleaning his brushes properly.

A further disagreement – caused by Barry claiming Brian had sworn at him near a local beauty spot – resulted in Barry arriving late one night at Brian's bungalow with drink detectable on his breath. More insults were traded in the garden and Barry began striking a portion of Brian's chainlink fencing with a wooden stake. At this point the police were called, and duly arrived, but not before Barry had thrown a pair of ornamental clogs over the disabled man's roof and on to the bonnet of a Vauxhall Astra owned by a local nurse called Barbara something – I can't remember her surname, sorry.

Barry received a caution for his outrageous behaviour, and was let off lightly in my view. But the story doesn't end there. One night, a month later, Barry was watching videos in his bedroom when there was a knock on the front door. He answered it to find a young couple on his doorstep with a bottle of wine. Now normally that would be a nice thing to happen, wouldn't it, someone turning up with a bottle of wine? But Barry was still feeling low after his brush with the law and was in no mood to relax with strangers. You're probably wondering what's going on here, readers. Well I'll tell you. For a prank, Brian had put a card in the local newsagent's window advertising a wild party at Barry's house with all comers welcome. I don't understand that, do you? What a crazy thing to do. He's a bit of a sicko that Brian, wouldn't you say?

Forgive me, readers, but I just have to go and sign some autographs. Don't worry, I'm not going to wait for folk to approach me for my autograph – I'd be waiting all day! Instead, Ken's clever plan is for me to approach them and ask them if I can borrow a pen and a piece of paper. (If they haven't got any, no problem, I'll produce my own.) I will then sign an autograph, whilst making pleasant conversation (like big stars do to relax their overwhelmed admirers). 'Have you got any brothers and sisters?' I might say, or 'Are you originally from the area?', that sort of thing.

When the autograph is completed, I will hand it over with a flourish and say 'There – will that do you?' They might look a bit stunned at this point and even gaze at my signature incredulously. That's all to the good, Ken reckons. It'll seem like they just can't believe they've managed to get John Shuttleworth's autograph. Obviously, when we come to edit the Rockumentary we'll cut out the beginning bit where I ask them for a pen and piece of paper. But what an ingenious plan, don't you think, and foolproof in my view. I can't see anything going wrong with that one.

While Ken nips into the newsagent for a notepad and biro I'll let you read another of my letters, which fits neatly into the next section...

How to complain for personal gain

Hey, it rhymes, that title! Indeed, literature experts would probably praise it for its galloping metre, but, in doing so, they'd be trivializing what is actually a serious matter. I don't know about you, readers, but I have to complain a lot about bargain products that turn out not to be such a bargain after all. (A KitKat that was wafer free, for example, or a Walls' Magnifico that fell in half, soiling the midriff area of my trousers.) But I'm always glad that I do complain because usually I receive by return of post a voucher for £1.50 or thereabouts.

So you see, readers, how to complain is important because if you adopt the right tone you'll be quids in, and free to buy even more bargains and then be able to complain again and receive yet more vouchers. No! You mustn't do that, tempting as it is, because it's abusing the system and queering the pitch for genuine victims like myself.

Now, here's that letter I promised you. It's a funny one this, because it actually started off as a letter of gratitude and only turned into a complaint when something went horribly wrong.

500 Bus Stops

24th May, 1993

Dear Trebor Bassets,

Congratulations on creating what can only be described as the perfect travelling sweet. I'm referring of course to your Pascall Barley Sugar retailing at £1.09 for a half-pound bag.

The packaging is quite superb, I must say. Not the outside cellophane bag – that's quite ordinary – I mean the wrapper surrounding each individual sweet. Honestly, it feels like you're unwrapping a present from a friend every time you have one, which is a terrific feeling. The inner silver wrapper was unexpected and a luxury you'd associate with a high-grade creamline toffee, such as Bluebird or thingy and Bowser.

As for the barley sugar itself, well! It was small enough to move around easily in my mouth, yet large enough for me not to be at risk from accidentally swallowing it or perhaps getting it stuck in my windpipe which has happened with boiled sweets in the past.

The outer shell was smooth and blemish-free and did not splinter suddenly under tooth pressure as some inferior sweets are prone to do. Oh dear, having said all that, guess what's just happened? I've just opened one and it's in loads of little pieces. What's going on? I can't believe it, after the nice things I've been saying. Maybe I've been deluding myself and your barley sugars are no better than anyone else's. No. I'm sure that's not true and I stand by the complimentary things I've said, but tell me, please, what has happened with the splintered sweet which I now enclose for your technicians to analyse in the labs.

Yours baffledly,

J. Shuttleworth (Mr)

Hold on, readers, Ken's just come off his mobile phone and I need to borrow it to give the AA a quick tinkle to see what's happened to my car. When I rang Mary earlier, she said the garage didn't know anything about it, which is mildly disturbing. Oo – Ken's gone as white as a sheet.

'What's the matter, Ken. Didn't you phone the AA yesterday, like you promised?'

'I'm sorry, John. Financing a major rock tour – or even a minor one - is a very costly affair – '

'What are you saying, Ken?'

'We were on our way to Norway at the time. Drinks are notoriously pricey – about seven quid for a pint of lager, you know?'

'What have you done with my car, Ken?'

'I scrapped it, John.'

'You did what?'

'I got a very good price for it considering its condition.'

'How much?'

'Fifty pounds.'

'You sold my car for fifty quid?'

'Here, take it, John. It's all yours.'

'I've just counted it, Ken, and there's only forty here.'

'Well, I've deducted my commission, obviously.'

'I don't believe it, Ken. How could you do that?'

'I'm sorry, John. Sorry I did the wrong thing. Maybe I should have consulted you first.'

Isn't that the most dastardly deed you've ever heard of, readers? It must be, surely. I'll be reeling from the blow of that piece of news for some time to come, I should imagine. What I don't understand is why Ken went on the attack. His actions were indefensible and yet he started having a real go at me, saying I didn't appreciate him and that his other clients' careers are suffering because of my tour. That may be true, but it doesn't explain why he suddenly stormed off the bus saying that I was no longer on his rostrum and that I'd have to seek alternative representation.

I've been sitting on a park bench for the last half-hour trying to

500 Bus Stops

make sense of everything. I tried feeding the ducks with my Tracker bar but even they didn't want to know me. (There was someone else feeding them though, and it looked like he had some very tasty buns.)

I've lost everything – my car, my agent, my chance to become famous – because clearly the tour can't continue without Ken (he's got the itinerary in his bumbag you see). I've even lost my tea, because that Tracker bar should have been for me really.

I shall be sad to leave Ken's stable. He's got quite an impressive rostrum, you know – even without me. I've kept quiet about the others till now, which was a bit mean of me, because they're all top class acts and I wish them well. I sincerely do.

Ken's clients

Little known, yet ever rising in popularity – Ken says – is Leeds-based speciality act Julie Satan. She wears a basque and a leather gauntlet and brandishes a broadsword whilst miming to backing tapes. She also sticks her tongue in and out like a viper, which sounds quite clever.

On a more sinister note Julie nearly killed Ken once. The two had met up in a bar to discuss Julie's future. To ease the tension, Ken cracked a joke. It must have been a slightly cheeky one because, upon hearing the punch-line, Julie flicked her wrist in the manner of a drag queen and said 'Oo, ducky' or 'Get you' – something like that.

Unfortunately, Julie's fingers made contact with Ken's windpipe which caused Ken to begin choking violently. Julie misread the situation and thought Ken was laughing at his own joke. She said 'Hey, you shouldn't be laughing at your own joke', which is fair enough, because you know, you shouldn't. But he wasn't, readers, he was fighting for his life.

Sammy Martini is an exciting young prospect – a personality vocalist with a quicksilver wit. He also does impressions, and he shrewdly announces who he's going to impersonate. You know, he says 'Chris Eubank, ladies and gentlemen!' and then does the impression. Straight afterwards he tells the audience again who it was 'That was Chris

Strangeways

Eubank, ladies and gentlemen, thank you!' That's very clever when you think about it because some people won't have recognized the voice, and may have already forgotten who Sammy said he'd be doing.

Rory Bremner should take a leaf out of Sammy's book – he rattles those impressions off far too quickly; he doesn't seem to have access to any wigs or facial hair; and ultimately you wind up feeling cheated. And you don't know half of them. I keep looking out for Mavis Riley, but maybe he can't do her. Sammy can, supremely well. He's quite a character. He works at Kwik-Fit, you know. As you approach him he

'Have you seen my agent?' Outside a Manchester music shop.

adopts a boxing stance as if he's about to hit you. Then, at the last second, he pulls away, which is a good job, because he's a big lad.

Janet le Roe is another of Ken's signings. Her real name's Janet Roebottom, but Ken very cleverly suggested dropping 'Bottom' and putting a 'le' in front of Roe. It works a treat, I'm sure you'll agree. Janet plays acoustic guitar and has taught herself how to do finger-picking – a fantastic feat. I'm quite envious, I wish I could do that. Mind you, Janet keeps her head down too much in my view, and often fails to establish eye contact with her audience. Moreover, she plucks the strings too softly, and, at the drop-in centre, tends to be drowned out by the table soccer. Clearly she requires amplification.

Before he deserted me, Ken expressed concern for Janet's well-being. Apparently she's had her guitar stolen and was devastated. I'm wondering myself whether it might not be still in the lock-up behind a trestle table. Unfortunately, we won't know if that's the case until Tuesday morning when Mrs Bonnington returns from South Africa (she's got the key, you see).

Oh, no! I've just had a terrible thought. What if my performance in Ken's star-grooming programme was so abysmal (although the autograph signing went quite well, you'll be pleased to hear) that Ken has secretly decided to offer my spot in the open-air rock festival to Janet le Roe, in the hope that this will cheer her up, and make her forget about her recent loss.

'Ah, but she's without her guitar, John, and so is unable to perform', I hear you cry. Well, you're wrong there, readers. She can sing acappella and does a good impression of Joanna Lumley. Ken knows this, and may, even as I write, be liaising with Janet on his mobile phone about dressing-room arrangements, the length of her turn, etc. I may be very wide of the mark – perhaps Ken did a runner because he felt so ashamed at scrapping my car. But if I'm right, it's a wicked plan and Ken and Janet must be stopped.

Excuse me, readers, while I go and ask a few people if they know of any open-air rock arenas in the vicinity.

Well, nobody did, but it doesn't matter because I'm delighted to report that errant agent Ken Worthington and I have been reunited in a second-hand music shop. Yes, it's true, readers. I'd popped in here to buy some batteries for my organ and to check out a small fawn-coloured amplifier I'd spied in the window (just in case I found the venue and my organ's built-in speaker didn't prove loud enough amongst all those cheering youngsters). Then, who should I see trying out a second-hand clarinet but Ken. It was a super sight, and a huge relief to realize he hadn't given my spot in the festival to Janet le Roe after all. Under the circumstances it seems only right and proper to

500 Bus Stops

give Ken the £40 he gave me earlier so he can purchase the clarinet – although, right now, Ken appears to be spurning my generous offer.

'What's the problem, Ken?'

'I can't accept it, John. This forty pounds is yours. To help you buy a new car.'

'Please accept it, Ken. I heard you play, and it was beautiful.'

'I was only busking, John.'

'Maybe so, but at least you didn't go red in front of the assistant. Perhaps you're ready to make a comeback, Ken.'

'Oo, I don't know about that.'

'All right then, what if I were to offer you a support slot on my tour?'

'That's a kind offer, John, but maybe I'll just come on at the end and do a little solo.'

'Oh, Ken, would you? I'd love it if you did.'

'Come on then, John, let's go and find the rock festival. The crowd'll be getting restless.'

Good old Ken. I knew everything would turn out fine in the end. Or did I? I didn't really, readers, no. But it has done, anyway. Or has it, in fact? We're back on the bus, thundering once more towards the Peak District, but Ken's behaving very strangely. He keeps whispering into his mobile phone and craning his neck in an anxious manner, as if he doesn't know where he's going. I sincerely hope that's not the case. Oh, well, who cares! Not me. I've done enough worrying for one day. I propose to spend the rest of the bus journey jotting down the last of my tips for bargain seekers. (Sorry to keep you waiting for these, readers, but thanks for being so patient.)

Beware of superbargains

Sometimes what appears to be a fantastic bargain is nothing more than an elaborate hoax. Several months ago I was perusing the miscellaneous section of our local free paper. I was mildly tempted by 'Endurance saddle – £18', but as I haven't got a horse I allowed my eyes to wander on to 'Single sandwich toaster, requires attention – £2'. Interesting, but we're already in possession of a toaster, and ours works fine, thank you. 'Sylvanian Families, hose and bakery' held my attention for a wee while, as did '6-inch plastic whale, 50p' until, hang on, I thought, whales are supposed to be large creatures, aren't they? Owning a tiny one could lay me wide open to ridicule from friends and family alike, so I didn't bother with that one either.

Then I saw it – 'Large rabbit hutch – £1'. *One pound!* It had to be a joke. I was trembling as I wrote down the vendor's address. As I jumped into my car, I remembered that actually we already own a rabbit hutch – and we haven't even got a rabbit any more because it died. Still, if this hutch was sufficiently large maybe we could store our hutch inside it, thus protecting it from the elements. If not, we could always adapt it for use as a compost heap – the chicken-wire front being ideal for aerating the rapidly decomposing matter. The sleeping quarters could be retained as a second compost heap, or, if not, the plywood partition could be removed and turned into a snow-scraper – once a sturdy handle had been attached. All these possibilities were racing through my mind as I sped to my destination (whilst observing the speed limit at all times, naturally).

I parked my car and ran up the drive to the front door. I rang the bell, but there was no reply. I tried again, but still there was no answer. A brief stroll around the perimeter of the property was highly revealing. The rabbit hutch wasn't there. So where was it then? Could it have been sold already? Impossible – the newspaper had only come on public sale that very afternoon, and my response to the ad had, as I'm sure you agree, readers, been breathtakingly swift. I rang the doorbell a final time. Was it my imagination or did I hear a stifled whisper coming from inside the property?

It suddenly dawned on me. There was someone in there all right. They just weren't answering the door. They'd realized – too late in the day – that they'd massively under-valued the rabbit hutch, and had panicked. Rather than be honest with prospective purchasers and risk upsetting them by saying that they now wanted at least a fiver for it, they'd decided it would be safer to pretend the hutch didn't exist, or themselves for that matter, and so had carried the hutch into the house, using it (if they had any sense) to barricade the door against the world and his wife. An understandable ploy, but, goodness me, what a bunch of cowards, eh readers?

'Visual stimuli' to spice up my live act. (The skeleton is Ken's, incidentally.)

Sharing a joke (not a blue one, obviously) with a group of cub scouts.

Well, no doubt you're curious to know how the rock festival went, and indeed whether or not we ever even found the open-air arena. Well, we did, and it went extremely well, thank you. It wasn't quite what I expected, mind you. There were no bare ladies, no love drugs, and they didn't wave their cigarette lighters in the air when I sang Foreigner's 'I want to know what love is'! That's because they were all too young to smoke. They were cub scouts, you see, camping in a field near Hathersage.

My initial disappointment evaporated when Ken reminded me that cubs need music in their lives like everyone else, and anyhow they'd be scouts before long, and venture scouts eventually. When I sang 'If you're happy and you know it, waggle your woggle' you could have cut the atmosphere with a penknife. Honestly, it was a fantastic climax to a very strange, very exhausting day.

See you in the morning, readers. Lights out, please! Only joking. No I'm not actually. Put your lights out, please. Thank you.

Blue John

How To Cope With Unruly Children and What's a Shuttleworth?

Good morning once again, readers. I don't know why but sole agent, Ken Worthington, has woken up in a very cheeky mood, and has been singing my controversial fun track 'Up and down like a bride's nightie' aboard a packed bus. I've tried to shush him, but he's in a defiant mood. What a naughty man. Or is he, readers? Close examination of the song's lyric reveals that it's actually all about violent mood-swings and isn't a blue number at all. Let me sing you a snatch and then you'll be able to judge for yourselves.

I'm up and down like a bride's nightie
I'm up and down and I don't know why – ee – oo –
I'm happy and then I'm blue

I don't know why I feel so high
Then suddenly go so low
I don't know what to do to stop
My moods from swinging
From ecstatic to stinking and back –

I'm up and down like a bride's nightie
Up and down and it's most unlike me – oo –
I'm happy and then I'm blue
Maybe it has happened to you

'You like that number, don't you, Ken?'

'I do, John. It'd be nice for Tori Amos, Mike and the Mechanics – someone like that.'

'Or Clannard, possibly, Ken, because a lot of their material is a bit gloomy, isn't it? It'd be nice to hear them attempt something in a lighter vein.'

'It would, John, yes. You can sing it to the A&R man when we get to London.'

'I will, but we'll show them the video first though, eh?'

Yes, indeed, readers, we're high as kites today and can you blame us? We're on our way to the metropolis with a promotional video of last night's show with which we hope to woo record company chiefs. The hard slog has paid off. My act is now finally honed and I am ready to cut a disc.

And it can be no accident that I am suddenly becoming aware of the perks of pop success. Ken has secured (finally) a luxury tour bus for the trip. Well, it's a National Express coach really, but it boasts neck-rests and full toilet facilities, and he even paid for my ticket, as well as his own. And – oo, goodness me, Ken is being generous today! He's just handed me a baseball cap. I'm presuming it's a gift. Perhaps I should ask him.

'Is this for me, Ken?'

'It is, John. Well, you've got to look the part. Actually, why don't you put it on backwards? It looks more stylish that way.'

'Maybe so, Ken, but the buckle might leave an impression on my forehead. Have you considered that?

'Oo – no, I didn't, John. Sorry.'

'I mean, if I had a piece of lint I'd be laughing because I could place it behind the buckle to protect my forehead. But that's one thing I forgot to pack.'

Well, readers, while Ken is searching for some lint I may as well dispense some more handy hints. What's today's topic to be? Entertaining those cubs last night naturally made me nostalgic for my own Wolf Cub days. But it also reminded me that youngsters are sometimes prone to unruly behaviour and require close supervision at all times. Ken tells me that after last night's show a group of cubs surrounded him and began flicking towels at his afro.

Ken displayed great courage in remaining still throughout the ordeal – or was he just frozen with fear? Possibly, and yet once the attack was over Ken squared up to the ringleader with his chest puffed out and gave the lad a well-deserved roasting.

Full marks to Ken, and yet if he'd been armed with the information I'm about to impart, a confrontation might have been averted altogether.

Blue John

How to Cope with Unruly Children

Being a father of two ebullient teenagers, and a part-time volunteer worker at the local drop-in centre, I'm well qualified to instruct readers on all aspects of youth care.

Not that my kids are prone to unruly behaviour, you understand. If you're thinking that then you're very wide of the mark, readers.

Having said that, I've just remembered Darren threw a party once without our prior knowledge. It was a Sunday afternoon and me and Mary had gone to visit a stately home with ornamental gardens near Leek, Staffordshire. I didn't fancy it myself, but Mary had been given a voucher which entitled the holder to a free punnet of strawberries if you arrived before 3 p.m. It was a mad dash to get there before the deadline, and, at several points during the hundred-mile journey (while stuck in particularly bad traffic), we wondered whether we were doing the right thing.

We needn't have worried. We had the place to ourselves. I suspect the torrential rain had put a few people off, but you didn't even need to set foot in the gardens. In fact, we spent the entire afternoon indoors! You see, in the huge ballroom was an extensive range of fitted kitchens. What a fantastic surprise. It absolutely made our day. While Mary wandered around opening cupboard doors, I stuffed myself with strawberries and sipped filter coffee (free and unlimited) in the company of several blonde dolly-birds, whose green trouser-suits were a pleasant reminder of the dungarees worn by Homebase staff (but they were even snazzier, I reckon).

But what's all this got to do with Darren? Well, that evening we returned over the moon to discover that he'd had a party in our absence, the naughty lad. I found three cigarette stubs near the front wall, and the arm of the stereo was a bit bent – a big fat lad had sat on it apparently. So there'll be no parties in our house, not for a long time anyway.

Apart from that isolated incident our kids are as good as gold. And, given that today's advice is about children, I'd like now to talk a bit about

500 Bus Stops

them, if I may, while Ken and I sit cruising down the motorway to London.

But first an extract from my haunting rock anthem 'The Isle of Arran':

I've got a son called Darren
And a daughter whose name is Karen
Without them my life would be barren
Like living on the Isle of Arran

Now Darren used to be a nuisance
But since he started work at the off-licence
He's out until twelve, his hair is nicely gelled
And we get on really well
Yes he's a true prince

Yes, Darren works in the evenings at Victoria Wine where he's doing very well – learning a lot about – erm – wine, obviously, and cashew nuts, that sort of thing. Recently he was approached by Augustus Barnet. He wanted to poach him, you see, but Darren wasn't interested. He's happy where he is.

Darren sleeps all morning then enjoys a late breakfast – 2.15 p.m., taken alone at the breakfast bar. Perched high upon a stool, he sensibly tucks a teatowel into his collar to protect his shirt from accidental spillage. Then he leaves the house at 3.30 p.m., in time to begin his shift at four.

You may be thinking he's a lazy lad sleeping in like that, but he isn't. You're very wide of the mark again, readers. You see, he often doesn't get home until the wee small hours because, after work, he tends to visit his friend Adam in his bedsit – rented, incidentally, with his parents' full approval – to watch a couple of war videos, and just generally chill out.

Darren has a cabin bed, incidentally, bunk-style with a ladder, and a useful study area beneath. It's a black ash, self-assembled unit which he's had since he was eleven. It's a bit small for him now, yes, but he feels safe in it, you know. Nevertheless, recently Darren has begun expressing an interest in purchasing a double mattress to be placed directly on to the floor, without a base or headboard. I didn't know this but, apparently, you can do that now. Good on you, son – nice one!

When Darren was little it was a different story. It's not that he was unruly – he just used to get on my nerves sometimes. We'd go for drives round the countryside in my Chrysler with Darren sat upon the special seat I'd made for him from $3/4$-inch ply, so he could see the cows and sheep properly. But, instead of displaying gratitude for his father's kindness, he'd be continually shuffling about and craning his neck to look at the back seat – although there was no one there. On occasions he'd even attempt to establish eye contact with me – a crazy thing to do with the driver of any vehicle. His appearance was irksome – he wore a brown tweed overcoat and a bulky woollen balaclava, even in the height of summer, which obstructed my view at T-junctions, and he always had a bag of toffees on his lap.

Once, when I was trying to turn left on the outskirts of Penistone, all I could see was a balaclava and a pair of chomping teeth. It was disgusting. There were glistening strands of toffee connecting the upper and lower set, and Darren was trying – through frantic gnashing – to separate them. It reminded me of a former neighbour's elderly poodle, and I felt ashamed that he was my son. I confiscated the bag and placed them securely in the glove compartment. Once he'd cried himself to sleep, it was most gratifying to be able to help myself at will to the remaining toffees, without Darren's prior knowledge.

Now what about my daughter, Karen. You'll be wanting to know all about her – I warrant. Well:

Karen plays the recorder
And composes pretty tunes to order
And when she was small
She threw some gravel at a wall
Though she thought she was alone
In fact I saw her

500 Bus Stops

'You are the Sunbeam of my life!' Me with the vehicle for which Darren's special seat was so lovingly crafted.

But I took no action. Well, she was only a toddler. That's what toddlers do, isn't it? She wasn't being unruly, not really, and, apart from the time she tried to escape on her rollerskates, Karen's been a model daughter. Yes, sometimes she flies off the handle for no reason (a bit like her mother) usually when I want to come into her room to check her curtain has been tucked correctly behind the radiator. And she won't play recorder on my demos any more, which is upsetting, but on the whole I'm very proud of her.

Indeed, when she was ten, Karen made a fantastic gesture. Inspired by Band Aid she insisted that the tangerine she normally gets in the toe of her stocking on Christmas Eve be redirected to the starving children of Africa. It's easy to scoff and say 'But there's no guarantee it would be distributed fairly'. To that, I would be forced to answer 'No, you're right, there isn't'. In fact, after we'd posted it, we didn't hear anything, not a dickie bird, so it could well be that it perished in the mail, or – more sinisterly – was intercepted by an army captain who gobbled it all up for himself, without even giving any to his men. You don't know, do you?

Recently Karen's started going ice-skating on a weekly basis with her friend, Hayley. Sometimes I go in my car to pick them up afterwards, and one time I was a bit early, so they were still on the ice. They were going round and round in the middle, holding hands and looking a bit forlorn. I couldn't believe it. I said afterwards 'That's no way to get a boyfriend, ladies. You should be at the edge of the ice, acting all bubbly, and letting the lads spray ice in your faces'. They didn't seem to believe me, but it's an established courtship ritual, isn't it?

Karen had a boyfriend, but she finished with him. I think it was because his voice was quite high and squeaky. It's a shame because he's a lovely lad, Howard is. He used to hold the wood nice and steady whilst I cut it with my tenon saw. Darren never did that – his eyes were all over the place, especially when I had a girlie calendar on the wall. I took it down because it's considered too blue now, isn't it, in a domestic environment? But back in the sixties and seventies every grown man had one in their workshop.

Oh, dear! Tragedy has once again befallen my National Rock Tour of the UK. As you know, we were supposed to be travelling to London to meet a top A&R man with a view to my cutting a disc, but Ken has gone and cocked it up again by putting us both on a coach to Leeds. Apparently he saw the 'L' on the front and assumed it said London. But it didn't, readers, it said blinking Leeds. I was busy unwrapping a Nuttal's Mintoe at the time, and so failed to spot the blunder.

'Egg sales are down!' The farm in the middle of the M62.

It is a grave error, and one that can't be undone. We are now speeding up the M62, moving further and further away from London, and any chance I'll ever have of becoming a major rock star. Having said that, the sight of a farm sitting between the east and west carriageways of the M62 has inspired me to write a new song in which I've compared my plight with that of this most unfortunate home-owner. It's called 'The Man Who Lived On The M62'.

Blue John

I'm thinking about my past
And silly things I've done
Things from which I've wanted to run

Once I planed a door
That was fouling on the floor
Now the wind comes whistling through
A gap that wasn't there before

A strip of beading I secured
With non-returning screws
Is I notice slightly proud
But there's nothing I can do

Life's a tricky trip
And no one gets a map
Every road you take may
Turn out to be a cul-de-sac
Too late to worry now
I can't turn back the clock
At least I can cross the road
To get to the corner shop

And I feel like the man who lives
On that farm which sits
In the middle of the M62
I thought it would be all right
Now I can't sleep at night
Some things you cannot undo

Well, it was lovely talking to you about my kids because they're very well behaved, but it's not teaching you about how to cope with unruly ones – which yours are presumably (or you'd have skipped this section). I'd like to help you if I can, so, without further ado, let me leave Ken to sort out his dreadful cock-up while I dispense some parental advice.

Nip naughtiness in the bud

One Saturday morning my little grandniece, Michaela, came a-calling. Without even waiting to have her anorak and her pompon hat removed, she went straight to the fruit bowl, took out a banana, and started peeling it. Instead of issuing the command of 'No!', reinforced by a light smack, her mother, Dawn (my niece) said 'Oo, clever girl, Michaela. Well done!'

Blue John

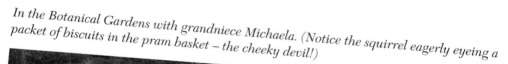

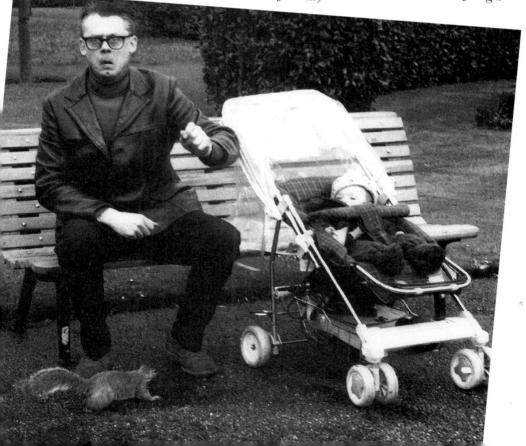

In the Botanical Gardens with grandniece Michaela. (Notice the squirrel eagerly eyeing a packet of biscuits in the pram basket – the cheeky devil!)

Yes, it was clever, she was only two at the time, but that's not the point, is it? You don't do that. Do you help yourself to fruit from the fruit bowl without asking, readers? Of course not. At Christmas time, yes, but not at any other time of the year. I couldn't believe it, and Mary was looking daggers at her. You can't imagine the bad feeling that incident caused in our house, and still causes even now – if it's mentioned, which it rarely is, for obvious reasons.

One of the biggest crimes perpetrated by toddlers is theft of food. This must be dealt with swiftly and severely. If you catch your youngster climbing a chair to gain access to the biscuit barrel, creep up behind them and shout 'No!' whilst banging the worktop hard with the flat of your palm.

The shock of this may cause the youngster to lose their footing and tumble to the ground, so be ready to withdraw your palm and place it with the other hand under your child's armpits. (Make sure you don't tickle them at this stage, or they will associate pleasant sensations with their naughtiness and repeat the crime.)

Then take them to the window and point out something exciting going on outside – a car reversing into a drive, for example, or workmen carrying out non-essential repairs to a neighbour's carport. This will distract the child and make them forget all about feeding their tummy – unless, of course, they're starving because you've forgotten to give them their breakfast. If this is the case, you should seriously consider whether you're qualified to be a parent. Perhaps your child would be better off placed under local authority care. Well, maybe that's a bit extreme but, you know, please remember to give them their breakfast in future, all right?

There's a little boy at Mary's school whose behaviour is showing cause for concern. The other dinner-time he was in the playground, holding Mary's hand, when he suddenly pointed to the sky and said 'My daddy's up there'. Naturally Mary was very distressed to hear this and did her best to comfort the little lad saying 'Ah! Has he gone to heaven then, love?' But the lad then laughed and said 'No, he's flying a helicopter'.

Well, Mary checked with the caretaker, who knows the boy's parents, and he assured Mary that he couldn't have been up in a helicopter. He doesn't even have a pilot's licence. He's a local joiner who, at the time, was working in the immediate vicinity. So clearly the boy was lying through his teeth. But why, oh why, did he spin such a yarn? I reckon he's a bit of a sicko, don't you, putting Mary through all those different emotions. All right, he's only six, but even so, it doesn't bode well for the future, I reckon.

Talk to your child, read them stories (if you can find the time), and play games with them. Ping-pong, for instance. But don't smash every return, however tempting. Do a few gentle lobbing shots that will enable them to attempt a winning stroke. Once they've won a few points they'll relax and take you into their confidence. Who knows, they may even tell you why they are being unruly! Oo – hang on, readers – Ken wants a word.

'I'm sorry to interrupt you, John. But I've got it sorted now. We're getting off at Leeds and getting a coach to London. Is that all right?'

'I suppose so, Ken.'

It isn't really, readers. But at least I'll be able to jot down lots more handy hints before we reach the capital. You might think I'll be running out of them soon, but fret ye not. I've plenty more. Here's the next one.

Reward good behaviour

I once took a group of hyperactive youngsters to see a horse in a field. (It was a reward for putting the ping-pong table away in record time!) Although they didn't get a proper sighting of the horse (it was at the far end of the field hiding behind a bush) they none the less had a smashing time spiking their hands on the barbed wire fence and then going 'ouch!' – but laughing as they did. You know, they weren't seriously hurt or anything.

On another occasion, Mary, the kids and I were driving home after visiting the dentist, when we saw an ice-cream van parked on a grass verge. Our injections hadn't worn off so nobody really felt like an

My passport photo, 1972. (Taken because my father and I planned to attend the TT Races on the Isle of Man.)

ice-cream, but it seemed too good an opportunity to miss. Besides, I wanted to reward the kids for their impeccable behaviour in the dentist's waiting room (they sat bolt upright with their comics, and spoke in hushed tones even when the angelfish started fighting). So we parked up and, whilst Mary and Karen stayed in the car (Mary was cold and Karen still felt a bit groggy) me and Darren went and ordered four small 99s with raspberry sauce on. (No chocolate bits though, which was disappointing.)

To cut a long story short, Darren and I went back to the car with the ice-creams, once we'd paid for them, of course (we did the logical thing, incidentally, and carried two each) and we ate them there and then. I recall a feeling of supreme satisfaction as I stood with my foot resting on the doorsill and my elbows on the roof, licking my ice-cream whilst the cars were whizzing past. In due course, Mary passed me up a moist wipe. (I hadn't requested one. She just knew intuitively that it would be welcome at that point. And how right she was!)

It was one of those rare moments when we were all together in our nice clothes enjoying a family treat, and it'll probably never happen again, which makes it all the rarer; a golden moment to treasure.

Don't overdo kindness, or unscrupulous juveniles will take advantage and throw it back in your face. Last Christmas we went round to Joan Chitty's for a few drinks and assorted nibbles – placed conveniently on the sideboard. During the course of the evening I agreed to play hide-and-seek with her nephew, an unruly six-year-old named Thomas Ablewhite. We'd already had a run-in over a disputed segment of Chocolate Orange (despite being covered in little fingerprints it was delicious!) Anyway, I had to hide first, and, not wishing to alienate Thomas further, I chose an easily detectable hiding place – the linen cupboard.

Well, I waited and waited, but there was no sign of the little lad. After about fifteen minutes I had to open the door because the hot-water cylinder was making conditions unbearable (being Christmas time it had been set on constant) and I was in danger of passing out.

With the door open, it was now much easier for Thomas to find me, but he was still nowhere in sight. I was at the point of cursing him for being so poor at hide-and-seek, when I suddenly heard a child's sobbing coming from somewhere. After a brief splash-down in the bathroom to soothe my red cheeks, I began to search for the distressed child. (Obviously I didn't count to ten first as it wasn't officially my turn to seek.) I looked everywhere, but the little chap was nowhere to be found. And, by now, the crying – which would have made pinpointing his precise position a lot easier – had stopped. A worrying sign.

My father Bernard's passport photo. (Note: you don't need a passport to visit the Isle of Man, as we later discovered – after we'd decided not to go anyway.)

I hurried back to the lounge to summon up a search party for the unfortunate child when I noticed he was sitting on the blinking settee watching telly! All at once the events of the last forty-five minutes fell into place.

Thomas had begun his search, but then swiftly abandoned it in favour of watching Wallace and Gromit in *A Close Shave*. The sobbing I had heard was actually laughter at the antics of Nick Park's brilliant plasticine creations. And, finally, nobody had missed my presence because the story-line was so absorbing. I chuckled at the irony of it all, though I was a little annoyed as well. I shouted out 'Well, I'm back everyone!' and began to recount my strange adventure. But nobody was listening. Huh! Surely the film wasn't that good. But then I sat down and started watching it myself, and, within seconds, I realized that it was. It was brilliant, and I began laughing along with the others, forgetting all about my uncomfortable ordeal – until now.

Teenage tearaways

Some teenagers are a menace, wandering the streets, scratching cars and writing graffiti – which reminds me – I saw some lovely graffiti once in the toilets at Doncaster train station. It wasn't blue, I assure you. It said 'I'm Dave Tordoff. Always travelling and moving around the UK' which I thought was quite nice. 'Where are you today, Dave? Chapel-en-le-Frith, perhaps? And are you going somewhere different tomorrow? And, if so, can we come too?' No, I'm only joking, but he seems quite an interesting person, doesn't he? I'd quite like to meet him.

As an ex-security guard, I feel it my duty to keep a constant eye out for trouble. I read in the local paper the other day that the police are still hunting two youths who moved an antique wagonwheel a hundred yards from outside a pub after a late-night drinking spree. One's described as a ginger nut, stockily-built; the other is of Mediterranean colouring and was sporting a yellow Lycra top. Any information, please, to PC Alan Harker. He's dealing with this one, all right? I realize they may have caught them by the time you read this, and, anyway, you might not live in our area. Having said that, they may have taken refuge in a different locality, so keep your eyes peeled.

500 Bus Stops

I'm now sitting in the restaurant at Knutsford Service Station on the M6 having just spoken to Mary on Ken's mobile phone. She was putting a brave face on things, but it sounded distinctly like she wasn't coping without her husband. True, the gears on her bike are still functioning perfectly, and the breadbin door is no longer jamming, but our shower has developed a serious fault.

Apparently whilst in 'on' mode, the operator is faced not with a generous, even spray, but a miserly trickle. It sounds to me like the rose is blocked – but by what? A foreign body? Unlikely, the head was cleaned thoroughly and the rubber seal checked by yours truly only last month. Could calcification be the cause? Impossible! Our house is in a soft-water region – served by a reservoir situated in the Dark Peak.

No, readers. It's a complete and utter mystery, which will only be solved once I've returned home, and made a thorough investigation. But that means abandoning my rock tour at a crucial stage, and I can't do that, can I?

Of course, I can't – Ken would be devastated. But I have to confess something, readers, the further south we travel, the more my desire to visit the Smoke wanes. I'm missing the Derbyshire countryside and I've not spotted a garden centre all day. I'm even beginning to question whether I'm ready to enjoy chart success. Is Ken pushing his artiste too hard too soon, I'm asking myself? After all, the tour

KEN WORTHINGTON

INTERNATIONAL IMPRESARIO
for aspiring artistes

clients include:

SAMMY MARTINI, JANET LE ROE, ALAN the OPERA SINGER, JULIE SATAN & JOHN SHUTT

Ken's new business card. (Just look how he's spelt my name! Ken's defence is that he ran out of letters – a poor excuse.)

is barely under way. Wouldn't his efforts be better employed in buying me a pop-shield for my microphone (Tandy's do a nice one), or getting me some TV exposure, perhaps as a contestant in *Fifteen to One*, or even as a member of the audience on *Kilroy*. You know, I'd be quite happy with that really. Success should happen gradually, don't you think? All right, I'm no spring chicken, and time's running out for me. But I'm very patient, you know.

Oh, dear. Ken's just returned from having some new business cards printed on that machine by the Gents. He seems keen for us to get back on the coach and continue the trip to London. He's going to be very upset by what I'm about to say, but it can't be helped – some things have to be said.

'I'm not coming, Ken.'

'You what? You blinking well are. Now listen to me, John Shuttleworth. What's happening to you? I thought you wanted to be a star.'

'I do, Ken.'

'Well, act like you do. Smile. You're walking around like your budgie's been shot. All right, so there've been a few cock-ups along the way. There's bound to be on a tour of this complexity. But stop relying on me for everything. I can't carry you, John. You're too heavy.'

Ken's right. I am too heavy for him to carry – he's only a little man, don't forget that. But he has a big heart and a forgiving nature. I'm delighted to report that we are now winding our merry way once again through Derbyshire. And, although he's got a right face on him, I suspect deep down Ken's as relieved as me to be still in the North.

'Cheer up, Ken. You don't get scenery like this in London.'

'No, and you don't get record deals in Bamford!'

'Yes – but, Ken, what a relief to be off that motorway – not that motorways are as bad as those treetop protesters make out. Yes, they have a terrible impact on the environment, but they do give much swifter access to areas of outstanding natural beauty, don't they, Ken?'

'I suppose they do, John, yes – '

'And what about the rainforests? All right, we're not that bothered about them because we've got nice parks and garden centres we can visit, but the natives – they want some trees to look at as they go about their business, don't they? Mind you, you'd think they'd also want some open spaces for ball games, steam fairs, etc. You know, Ken, they shouldn't condemn it totally.'

'Hey, John – you're being like Sting, you know.'

'Am I, Ken?'

'You are. We're seeing a sensitive side to you which perhaps we should exploit further. Have you any more ecological tips you'd like to mention?'

'Yes, I have, actually. We should all try and switch our diets to organic foods that don't harm the soil like – erm… Tracker bars or Common Sense oats, that sort of thing.'

'Golden Graham's, John?'

'Mm – maybe – '

'Coco Pops? No, sorry. Erm – Mighty White!'

'Do you mind, Ken? I'm giving the tips.'

'Sorry, John. Please continue.'

'Thank you. Now you'll notice I'm drinking Lucozade Sport, Ken, which is isotonic and cares for the environment – what's happening! Where are you going, Ken?'

'It's our stop, John. Come on. Let's go and make an environmental video.'

What a terrific idea of Ken's, not least because it gives me the chance to sing my ecological number, which I wrote some time ago, but rarely perform for fear of alienating the audience, and sending them hurrying back to their rooms. It's got a highly controversial lyric, you see, readers, and calls for a radical rethink of the way we live our lives.

I'll sing it for you now, shall I, as a practice for the pop video Ken's planning to shoot.

Walk along the beaches
See the mucky surf
Now who caused this pollution?
There is no clear solution
And it's going to get much worse

Look at the rainforests'
Ever-shrinking girth
I know you like mahogany
But pine is just as lovely
And it doesn't cost the earth

Why are there always so many battles
taking place?
If the world was being run by you, me,
Or even Ken Worthington
There'd be no need to own a gun
Well, only in one case...
To start a running race
Come on, chase me!

And what about all these motorways
Carving up the turf
I know there is a traffic queue
But I'd rather wait a while, thank you
Than lose the land I love

What's the point in going faster
When the road leads to disaster
What's a shuttle worth?

Look into my spectacles
See the look of love
And maybe you'll see something else
A little reflection of yourself

But are we any closer
To solving the poser
What's a Shuttleworth?

What's a Shuttleworth?

That, readers, I'm sure you'll agree, is a clever title for my next advice section, which is all about how to care for the environment. But it can also be interpreted literally, i.e. 'What's a Shuttleworth?' That's to say – who am I? What do I want? Well, that's easy. I'm John Shuttleworth, versatile singer/songwriter, a family man from Sheffield, South Yorkshire, and currently I'm touring the country in a bid to secure international recognition – because that's what I want, you know, despite my doubts in the service station earlier.

But you knew that already, so let's ignore that interpretation of the title, shall we, and concentrate on the other one: 'What's a shuttle worth?' – you know, space travel and the Channel Tunnel, and all that. Is it worth the astronomical cost and indeed the cost to the environment? Can we save the world? Do we even want to? Of course, we do, but we must keep a clear head and not rush into doing things we might later regret.

Having said that, Sting, as Ken rightly says, is into the environment and he's a big pop star, so being concerned for the planet might help me in my quest for stardom. Ken's just been on the phone to Sting's record company actually, trying to fix up a meeting with Sting, with a view to us doing a duet together. It'll obviously have to wait until after the tour, but it's certainly worth giving it a go. He plays bass guitar, I think (which I've got already on my organ – it's built into the rhythm, you see) so, maybe, it'll be best if he just sings backing vocals, I'm not sure. I'll have a long chat with Ken about it nearer the time.

Now, before we go any further, can I say something? These conservationists – I'm sure they've got the nation's interests at heart, but sometimes they get it seriously wrong. When they say 'Stop building all these car parks!', it's clear they've not thought it through properly. You see, no more car parks – no more car boot sales. No more car boot sales – no more money raised to buy loft insulation material for needy pensioners. So it's not as clear-cut as we may have first thought, is it, readers? We need to strike a delicate balance between conservation on the one hand, and enhancing the quality of people's lives on the other.

Why is Man destroying the earth?

Well, I don't know. You know, I'm not an expert in these matters. But it strikes me there are a lot of selfish people out there who are putting their own interests first and not considering the impact their actions are having on our fragile planet – Ken Worthington, for example, who is sitting right next to me on this bus, having shot my ecological promo. (I should be all right because he's looking out of the window – oh, no, he's asleep. That doesn't surprise me. In order to get the necessary shots Ken had to negotiate steep and uneven terrain – exhausting for a small man in Cuban heels.) Well, at least I can now speak freely about Ken's crazy proposal to lay an ornamental path from his patio to the Hansel and Gretel chalet at the end of his garden. Basically, he seems to be just steamrollering the plans through with no consultation with any of his neighbours. All right, it's his garden, and he can do what he likes. But the point is some lupins will have to go – a ladybird's habitat, possibly. He should do a feasibility study first, shouldn't he? Then again, when all's said and done, a path'll look very nice there, and will provide superb access to his chalet in all weathers – negating the need for gumboots in heavy rain.

Litter-louts are a blinking nuisance. But hang on – are they? I regularly pick up sweet-wrappers from our front garden that have been discarded by local schoolchildren, and, whilst most are not very interesting, now and again I'll come across one that's quite rare – such as an Aztec wrapper. Remember them? Sadly, Aztecs are now a discontinued line, but happily the sturdy old-style wrapper had simply refused to disintegrate amongst the leaf mould and dog doodah.

The same used to be true of Bounty bars, but, several years ago, Mars of Slough did a dreadful thing and got rid of the cardboard strip – do you remember? I for one was incensed, and wrote the following letter to them, demanding an explanation:

30th March, 1988

Dear Mars of Slough,

I was heartbroken to discover that your Bounty bars – of which I have been a huge champion all my life – are no longer packaged with cardboard.

Do you think the two fragile bars no longer require the support of the cardboard? If so, I have to tell you that you are very wide of the mark because they do, you know.

Please reinstate the cardboard strip immediately. Apart from giving much needed stability to the Bounty – during handling and carriage – it also serves as a useful and attractive bookmark.

Perhaps you don't care what I think, but unless you wish my family to boycott all Mars products in the future, a letter of explanation plus a solemn promise that cardboard will be inserted inside the wrappers of ALL BOUNTY BARS MANUFACTURED AS FROM THIS MOMENT, would be appreciated. (Hope that last sentence makes sense.)

Kind regards,

John Shuttleworth

500 Bus Stops

Back to the environment. These treetop protesters from the Dingadong tribe (I like that name – it's catchy, it's immediate, and it's fun to say) claim they're protecting the trees, but what about the damage their hobnailed boots are inflicting on the more slender branches – not to mention their cooking pots? Also, I really don't think they should be putting sugar in the bulldozers' engines, do you? Surely it would be better employed at the local night shelter in the men's tea.

And while we're about it, why do they wear such dark gloomy colours. It makes little sense, especially during the summer months when the rest of us are sporting soothing pastel shades. Crazy, but there you go.

Actually, I shouldn't be too hard on them. Their hearts are in the right place. They just want to return to basic values and lead a quieter life – which is exactly how I felt a few years ago. They'd just started a bus service on our road for the first time. Loads of litter began appearing in our garden (not very interesting litter, neither, i.e. no Aztec or early Curlywurly wrappers), and inexplicably an orange Triumph Dolomite began parking outside our house on a regular basis (making reversing in and out of our drive rather tricky). Eventually, I'd had enough, and decided to seek an alternative environment in which to raise my family. As part of my enquiries, I wrote the following letter to the Lord Mayor of the Orkney Islands, Scotland:

Blue John

5th March, 1991

Dear Mayor,

I am very interested in living on a remote island, as I am sick to death of litter-bugs and rush-hour traffic.

My wife will be joining me, plus two teenage children, one boy and one girl. We are all, incidentally, fit and strong, and free from disease.

Is there a really remote Scottish island you can recommend for a family of four, with a school for Darren and Karen, and ideally one or two shops? I'm a security guard at present, and, although I expect I'll be employed in the farming sector, I will gladly take responsibility for the island's security, if called upon to do so.

Please don't think I am rushing into this blindly. As a lad I lived in the Derbyshire countryside, and once helped an injured magpie back to full fitness.

Hoping to hear from you ASAP with the official go-ahead, plus details of tenure and grazing rights, etc.

All good wishes,

John Shuttleworth & family

It's perhaps just as well the mayor didn't reply, because I failed to consult Mary about my proposal. I don't know what you think, readers, but I'm not sure she'd have been quite so keen as myself – though you never know.

No, it's not the Mayor of Orkney! It's me dressed as Alderman Fitzwarren.
(Hm, that washing line requires attention, wouldn't you say?)

How to clear a canal bank

I don't know about this one because I've never done it. I should think you just clear it, you know. It's a shame my daughter Karen isn't with us on the tour – she'd be able to play recorder solos during my shows for one thing – but she'd also be able to advise me here because she helped clear a canal bank once with her friend Maxine.

They were dressed as clowns as it was a fun event, and, at one stage, I was hoping to become involved dressed as Alderman Fitzwarren – the kindly man who befriends Dick Whittington when he first arrives in London, and whose daughter, Alice, Dick takes a shine to and eventually marries. Dressed thus, my job would have been to make merry on the bank whilst distributing bin-bags to the volunteers.

However, a few days before the event I did a recce of the site and, oh, no, it was uneven terrain. There were loads of brambles and detritrius everywhere – (is it detritrius or demetrius? Ken maintains it's demetrius, but that doesn't sound right to me).

The point is readers, my costume would have been hired, my tights would have been made of silk, you know. Can you hear what I'm saying? There were just too many potential hazards to justify me taking a chance. So I didn't do it in the end. I feel a bit bad about that, but at least I didn't miss out entirely. I was able to view the proceedings from the comfort of my car (parked strategically in the Jehovah's Witnesses' car-park) listening to the *Charlie Chester Show* with a bag of Werther's Originals on my lap.

Incidentally, Karen's not the only one leading the fight for a cleaner healthier environment. Darren recently enroled on a correspondence course in Sport and Nutrition. (That's environmental, isn't it? Well – sort of.) When he's completed the course he gets a degree, you know. That makes me laugh, because all these students – they spend three years or more beavering away for their degree, wasting taxpayers' money (actually they don't any more, do they, they have to pay for themselves which is much fairer). Darren has to pay for his degree, as well, but it only cost him £145 and he graduates in five months. Good on you, son – nice one!

But what about the starving millions?

It's a terrible thing, but in a way – because they don't have access to chocolate bars and fattening sweets such as sticky toffee pudding – there's no dilemma for them, no temptations to divert them from a sensible diet of rice, maize and skimmed milk. (They don't seem to do semi-skimmed out there, I notice, which is a shame.)

Isn't it ridiculous, though, that half the world is starving when we've got all these butter mountains just standing there doing nothing? It's probably difficult to get at them, I appreciate that. Climbing a mountain is never an easy task, and one made of butter would be a nightmare – those blokes with their shovels would be skidding all over the place. Climbing a grain mountain would be even trickier – your feet would just sink in. And it must be very tempting to abandon work and just throw yourself about in it – safe in the knowledge that your fall will be cushioned by millions of tiny grains.

I wonder what happens to starving people when they first start to get hungry. Do they see things in a funny way? I know I do when I'm a bit peckish. (It's my blood sugar level getting low, you see.) I don't hallucinate, but I do have a heightened state of awareness, which can cause me to misconstrue certain things I see.

A few years ago I went to see a fish at the botanical gardens that had come all the way from Columbia. It was rubbish. Honestly, it was just grey all over, I couldn't believe it. They'd said on Radio Sheffield 'Go and see this rare fish. It's only there for a week'. So I did. At that time, the aquarium shut at two. (It's shut all the time now, but there you go.) Anyway, I was running a bit late that day, so I skipped my lunch, you see!

Well, I saw the fish and was bitterly disappointed, as I say, so, to cheer myself up, I decided to walk down to the war memorial. In the distance I could see this bloke coming towards me, and he had his arms folded tightly across his chest. Blimey, I thought, he's doing some ju-jitsu – and I hurriedly prepared myself for combat.

However, as he got closer, I realized that what I thought were his arms were in fact two fawn stripes on his anorak. His hands were by his side clicking out a little rhythm. He seemed quite a nice lad, actually, and it's a shame he didn't want to stop and discuss the misunderstanding.

The same thing happened quite recently in Netto's car park. It was nearly teatime and I'd only had a Pot Noodle at dinnertime, so I was asking for trouble. I was about to drive off when I noticed a woman in an adjacent vehicle nutting the steering wheel repeatedly. Oh dear, I thought, she's forgotten a major item off her list. Then I looked again and realized that she was actually just trying to pull her seat forward. What a fool! I'd completely misread the situation. Needless to say, I made sure I had an extra big tea that evening!

Who cares anyway?

Once there were two flies stuck in a bowl of milk. One fly said to the other 'We've had it, you know. We'll never get out of here', and, of course, he sank and died without trace – you know, the body was never found. The second fly was more determined. He kept beating with his wings until eventually he had churned the milk into a pat of butter upon which he rose and made his escape.

Nice story, don't you think? Whether it's true or not I don't know – though I suspect it might be. And it brings us nicely on to the problem of apathy. Some people can't be bothered to try and save the world, or buy a red nose on Red Nose Day even, and that makes me very angry. These people would rather stay in and watch Sky Sport, or press their trousers if they're going out to play snooker with a work colleague. Don't get me wrong, these are both valid activities, but you've still got to find time to do some ecological work.

I feel a tiny bit guilty that I'm gallivanting round the country in pursuit of stardom, when I could be taking my empty Diet Sprite cans to the Save-A-Can Bank, or milk bottle tops to the Blind School – although, in my defence, there'd be no point because the Blind School's now an insurance company (they've done it up beautifully, you know).

I used to love taking a big bag of milk bottle tops on Mary's bicycle. I never adjusted the saddle to suit my height so, yes, I looked slightly comical, and was even the butt of a few jokes from passing paperboys. But who gives a monkey's? It was a nice run out for me, and the space vacated by the milk bottle tops (once deposited in the Blind School's porch) was filled on my return journey with a large bag of bran and oats for our Karen's rabbit, Suzy – who sadly is no longer with us, as I think I've already stated.

Hey, guess what, readers? I'm doing a benefit gig for the environment. That's right, I am. I don't know why I didn't think of it before, because it makes perfect sense. Well, I'm on the road anyway, and a pop concert's the perfect vehicle to raise funds for our threatened planet, and raise my profile – that's still at the back of my mind, I can't deny it.

But who is the show to benefit? It can't just be the environment, that's too vague. (The punters may get suspicious and withdraw their support.) It needs to be more specific, like a butterfly park, hedgehog sanctuary or something. I'll ask Ken if he's got any thoughts.

'Any thoughts, Ken?'

'How about a show to raise funds for a sack of bark chippings, John, to lay in a forest-trail car park – 'cos that helps in the suppression of weeds, doesn't it?'

'I believe it does, Ken, yes, that's not a bad idea. Or – could it be for guineapigs, perhaps?'

'If you wish, John. Any special reason?'

'Yes, Ken, I like guineapigs 'cos they're not afraid to establish eye contact and maintain it, which is lovely you know. I've not found that to be true of many other animals.'

'Very well, guineapigs it is. Now, John, where's the benefit gig to be held? A pet shop's the obvious choice, but – erm – '

'Look, Ken! Look – '

'Oh, yes, John. We're passing the Blue John Cavern.'

'Mmm – that'd be perfect, Ken, 'cos it's full of rocks and streams, which is ecological, isn't it?'

'And, of course, the Beatles started out in a cavern, didn't they, John?'

'They did indeed, Ken. Yes. There'll be a nice natural reverb, which'll enhance my vocal performance.'

'And you could sing a blue number like "Up and Down Like a Bride's Nightie".'

'How dough you dough?' Shaking hands with Tideswell's master baker.

'What for, Ken?'

'Blue – John! Don't you geddit?'

'Ha-ha! Very funny, Ken.'

'Come on then, John, let's get off at this stop.'

'Hold your horses, Ken. If we're going down a cavern we'll need Kendal Mint Cake and other emergency supplies, which should ideally include a can of WD40 to squirt on my organ keys to repel the cavern's moisture.'

'We'll stock up at the next village, John.'

'Good idea, Ken.'

And so, readers, we now find ourselves in the extremely pleasant Peak village of Tideswell, where the shopkeepers have proved so friendly that I've been compelled to write a song in homage to them. This number has a rugged sea shanty feel and ideally should be sung whilst wearing a smock and banging a tankard along in time, although I suspect you'll all just sing it in the normal manner. Or will you? You don't know the tune, so you'll probably just read it through in your head – which is a shame, but I understand.

When I go shopping in the North I find
The service is always splendid
A friendly smile you can count on while
The right change is being tended

If anyone dares criticize their wares
They never will be offended
If it needs repairs they'll even lend you theirs
While yours is being mended

Shopkeepers in the North are nice
They ask after your kids and wife
And when you've had a good chin-wag
They pop your provisions in your bag

While Ken works out how to put on his cagoule, and dubbins his Cuban heels, I'm going to sit down on a rock and finish my environmental tips. Don't worry readers, there's only a couple more…

Come on – let's save this fantastic planet of ours!

Please do something to help the fragile environment – even if it's just a drive to the reservoir to check the level. If you're not keen on environmental work – and I do understand some people not feeling too happy about it – then do some charity work instead. Organize a 'Sweets in a Jar' competition to raise funds to repair a local playgroup's video recorder, or a sponsored abseil down the side of the Out-patients' Department of the Teaching Hospital (please ask permission first). Help plan a mass pigeon release during your child's sports day, or approach your boss to see if he'll agree to be gunged.

Or follow the excellent example set by Darren's ex-colleague, Drew. He's only twenty-five, he should have the world at his feet, but he hasn't – he's got it on his shoulders. Drew earns a very poor salary at the photographic lab where he works, and his eyesight is deteriorating – he has to watch the prints as they go past, you see, so that's probably why. And his wife Wendy can't work – she's an asthmatic; their neighbours aren't very nice – they've got a Rhodesian Ridgeback that keeps jumping up at their little lad, Liam, and making him cry. Liam's nearly five, but he's still not talking. He says 'Me hungry'. You know, he's like a caveman.

Drew and Wendy have been out of Sheffield only once in the last three years when they went to Huddersfield to see Boy George, but even that was a huge let-down (he didn't have a dress on or make-up or anything, just a scruffy T-shirt and khaki fatigues. What a swizz!). And the new neighbour on the other side is a butcher and he has the washing machine going all night long (washing bloody aprons). The final straw was when a planner called from the town hall and told them to take down their new fence because their garden is a public right of way!

Yet, despite all these setbacks, Drew somehow manages to keep his

500 Bus Stops

chin up and enjoy his life. During this year's *Children in Need* he rang up Radio Hallam and pledged ten pounds if anyone would ring in and sing Bryan Adams on air – but it had to be in a funny voice, you know, which sounded a smashing idea. I wasn't listening unfortunately, but if I had been I'd have sung it as Frank Spencer: 'Look into my eyes, Betty!' – like that, you know.

Unfortunately, readers, there were no takers, so his tenner was safe. Still, what a fantastic gesture, and what an example to us all. Take heart from that, readers. The Earth may be dying, but there's still some lovely, lovely people knocking about.

Well, I performed my benefit gig for guineapigs, but the management of the Blue John Cavern charged us to enter which was a bit mean spirited of them, I thought. I was rather miffed with them about that. But not as miffed as I was with Ken Worthington when he suddenly took fright and fled with his camera (he saw a shadow on the cavern's roof which resembled a hooded axeman) leaving me to run the show on my own, and without any permanent record of what was a fine performance. It was, readers, not bad at all. They were a very attentive audience – apart from one bloke with a torch who talked all the way through the show.

I know earlier I was planning on travelling home today to be with my family – but I've changed my mind. Sorry, Mary, but the shower will have to wait. Tonight I'm going to sleep out in our Karen's fun tent that she so kindly lent me. It's a nice way of demonstrating my continued support for the green movement despite setbacks, but it's also the best way of avoiding a big taxi fare – we missed the last bus back to Sheffield, you see.

Not that I'd even be thinking of going home if it wasn't for Ken. He's the one who's missing his home comforts. And watching him struggling to erect the tent, it's clear that he learnt nothing during his time spent with the cubs. He's not cut out for camping life – his stylish clothes and afro requiring far more maintenance than is possible in an outdoor

Blue John

situation. Hang on a minute, readers. It looks like Ken's given up on the tent and is about to do yet another runner.

'Excuse me, Ken. Where are you going this time?'

'Somewhere I can enjoy some proper hospitality, John.'

'What do you mean by that, Ken?'

'A man gets lonesome on the open road, John.'

'Oo – does he now?'

'You see, John, normally a rock tour will attract groupies, but for some reason on this tour they haven't materialized.'

'I should think not. Wash your mouth out, Kenneth. Come back! Don't you want to save the environment, Ken – I thought you did?'

'Right now I want a Malibu and a cheese toastie, John. I've had enough of the environment for one day. It can get a bit boring, you know – even Sting realized that!'

'The perfect venue'. The Blue John Cavern provided spooky lighting, superb natural reverb, and an attentive audience (apart from a bloke with a torch who chattered incessantly).

Well, there's nothing for it, readers, but to have my supper and then get to bed. What have we got? There's some Kendal Mint Cake left – quite a lot actually – two fun-size Lion Bars, and a mini pork pie. And I might wash them all down with a can of Diet Lilt – that's environmental, isn't it – the Caribbean, you know. Actually, Ken's right, it can get a bit boring.

I could be at home now sitting on a bar stool with a hot milky drink, or settling down in the lounge with Mary to watch *Crimewatch Update*. But I'm not, and, while Ken is doubtless whooping it up with some dolly-bird in a local bistro, I've got to make myself comfortable in a draughty tent. At least I'll have a bit more room now Ken's not here – only a bit though, because he's not a big chap, as you know. Oo – excuse me. We've a trespasser on the field. I'll give you three guesses who it is.

'You didn't get lucky then, Ken?'

'No, but I found a nice tandoori, John. Do you want some tarka dal, John?'

'I do not, Ken. I've just brushed me teeth. Neither do you. It's too late to be eating rich food – it could lead to digestive problems in the early hours.'

'Wrath of Khan!'

I'm genuinely concerned, actually, readers, that Ken might produce unpleasant odours during the night, which, in a confined space, might prove intolerable. He has a reputation for doing this, you see. Many years ago, whilst on holiday with his then wife, Rhiannon – who was (let's not forget) the harpist who accompanied Ken on *New Faces* in '73 – Ken developed a serious digestive disorder which ruined Rhiannon's night – and indeed the rest of the holiday.

If I close with a rendition of my song 'Eggs and Gammon', which is based on the incident, you'll understand what I mean. Ken has sportingly agreed to accompany me. Join in yourselves, readers, when you feel confident.

'Hey, John, it's a bit cheeky this song, don't you think?'

'No, Ken, it's fine. It's a fun track and, anyway, if it's too rude, we can just stop and think of something else to do, can't we? You know, it's not that important.'

'I suppose not, John, no.'

Ken had some eggs and gammon
At a restaurant in Rhyll
Then he went with his wife, Rhiannon
To the campsite on the hill
The night was very windy
Though outside it was still

Eggs and gammon
Poor Rhiannon
Ken had wind
Eggs and gammon
Poor Rhiannon
Ken's bad wind

They opened up the tent flaps
But the smell it seemed to stay
So they tightened all the guy ropes
Just in case they blew away
They saw a daddy-longlegs
Get on his knees and pray

Eggs and gammon, etc.

And in the morning
The storm it did subside
Ken went to the doctor's
And some medicine was prescribed
What of the daddy-longlegs?
Well, I'm sorry to say he died

Camping's all very well, but I'd have preferred to sleep in Doreen Melody's camper van. (Note the sturdy chrome ladder – giving direct access to the roof.)

Oh eggs and gammon
Poor Rhiannon
Ken had wind
Eggs and gammon
Poor Rhiannon
Ken's bad wind – (Oo – pardon me, Vicar!)

In view of Ken's history I've half considered insisting he sleeps outside the tent tonight – or perhaps in that gap between the flysheet and the inner tent – but you know something, readers, at the end of the day, you can't care about the earth and the planet, and ignore the people on it, can you? Goodnight!

Blue John

How to Cope With Divorce and Miditations: How to be happy in a sad, sad world

Good morning everybody! Have you had your breakfast yet? I've not, but I'm about to so you'll have to excuse me in a minute while I go and eat it. It looks like I'll be breakfasting alone though, because Ken Worthington's still snoring away in his sleeping bag – the lazy bones.

'Ken, wake up, it's breakfast time.'

'Leave me alone, John. I'm trying to sleep.'

It sounds like Ken's got a hangover. Hardly surprising – because he downed a four-pack of lager during our bawdy singsong last night and I suspect he had a few more in a local hostelry beforehand. Still, a sore head is no excuse for a lie-in.

When I was a lad at Scout camp, any late-risers were carried forcibly to the breakfast table in their sleeping bags, and tipped out before the assembled throng. It was very humiliating – unless you had winceyette pyjamas on, like I did. But one lad had little undies on – like a thong, you know – very unusual in those days. We weren't quite sure how to react, you know. Anyway, if Ken doesn't get up soon, I shall be forced to employ the Scouting method, and expose him in his full morning glory.

'Ken – come on. It's half-past nine.'

'Precisely, John. No self-respecting rock artiste rises before noon.'

'Rubbish, Ken. What about Mick Jagger? He's always up at the crack to go for a jog, which is what I'm about to do, incidentally. And Roger Whittaker – I think he's another early riser.'

You see, readers, life on the road takes a heavy toll on the rock 'n' roll fraternity and it's important we stay fit. See you in a while!

Well, I'm back and feeling extremely foolish. Perhaps you didn't spot my mistake, readers, but if you didn't I have to say you're almost as big a fool as me. No, that's a bit harsh. I'm sorry. I just can't believe I left a lit primus stove unattended, which you should never *ever* do. Luckily Ken smelt burning and managed to avert a disaster – well done, Ken! But the ordeal has left him pale and groggy and in no fit state to continue the tour.

Not that I'm not keen to get back home to Sheffield. I'm missing my wife and kids and the DIY tasks are mounting up – the blocked shower-rose being the top priority.

Nevertheless, I'd very much like to end the tour with one big last booking. But can I rely on Ken to secure it? He's not a well man, and in a melancholy mood, still smarting, I reckon, from last night's rendition of 'Eggs and Gammon'. This has clearly rekindled desires for his ex-wife, Rhiannon.

500 Bus Stops

Ken and I have now left the campsite and are aboard a bus, bound I'm not sure where – though it's going roughly in the Sheffield direction. A moment ago we passed a churchyard in Calver and, as we did, Ken pointed out the gravestone he hid behind to view the wedding ceremony of Rhiannon and the man she'd rejected Ken for (more of him shortly).

I'll have to have a word with Ken. These morbid musings aren't doing his confidence any good at all.

'You mustn't dwell on the past, Ken.'

'I want to, John.'

'No, Ken. You must look to the future – immerse yourself in your work. You've a healthy stable of artistes who look to you for further successes. Any thoughts on tonight's final engagement, then?'

'I can't be thinking about that at the moment, John. You're so lucky. You've got a wife and a family to go home to. What have I got?'

'You've got a car, Ken. Which is more than I have since you sold my Austin Ambassador for scrap.'

'I know. I feel bad about that, John. But what can I do?'

'Well – you could give me your car, Ken. That would make you feel less bad about it, and I won't say no.'

'Mmm – nothing would help, John. I need a lady in my life. I think that's the problem. But nobody understands…'

'Don't cry, Ken.'

'I'm not, John. I think I've caught a chill.'

'You're certainly coming down with something, Ken. You look terrible. Let's get off at the next stop and have a campacinno. It's the Plague Village of Eyam, look, where you, Mary and myself had that memorable night out in a carvery.'

Well, we're in a teashop now, readers, and, whilst Ken's perked up a bit, he's definitely got a fever and is sneezing repeatedly. There's even a red blotch on his face. I realize I'm describing the classic symptoms of the bubonic plague that claimed so many lives in London in the 1600s. But there were isolated outbreaks, too – notably the one here in the picturesque village of Eyam. But it can't be the plague. Can it? I mean, for reasons you're familiar with, we didn't get to London on this tour and we've only just arrived in Eyam.

Having said that, I remember reading somewhere that germs can remain dormant for centuries, only to strike again with even greater ferocity. Another thing: the plague was carried by a flea, wasn't it? Now fleas are quite good at jumping, and with Ken being fairly short, one could easily have jumped up into his open mouth. Perhaps I'm being a bit fanciful here, readers? Still, as a precautionary measure, I'm going to pop to the pub across the road and buy Ken a medicinal Malibu – that should cheer him up.

Well, I'm back again, and whatever Ken's ailment was, it can't have been that serious. Certainly he was well enough to down three Irish coffees and a coconut macaroon in my absence. And then flee the teashop without paying the bill. (By the way, you'll be relieved to learn that the characteristic rosy ring on Ken's cheek was nothing more than raspberry jam from his tea cake. I forgot to tell you that. Sorry!) Anyway, upon my return, I was presented with a hefty bill, and, despite a thorough search of the immediate vicinity, I have been unable to trace Ken.

It's a tragedy because I've got some fantastic news to tell him. The pub is holding a live music night, with all-comers welcome. After a long conversation with the landlord he's agreed that I can appear with star billing, and the other performers come on before me as my support acts – well, the landlord said he'd think about it. To be honest he wasn't at all keen at first, but, once I'd explained I was on the last leg of a national rock tour and that my organ boasted a hundred rhythms including Argentinian Folklore and Fantasy Island, he visibly warmed to my plan.

'You're booked!' Rounding off negotiations with the landlord of the Miner's Arms, Eyam.

So, you see, I've secured the last big booking without Ken even having to raise a finger – but the silly fool doesn't know. Well, it's his loss. I shall carry out the engagement without Ken's professional guidance.

Oh, no! I don't want to alarm you, readers, but I've just seen something on the back of that bill – a very worrying message: SOS. It can mean only one thing. The pressures of the tour, and being a victim of unrequited love, have become too much for Ken and he's wandered off to do himself a mischief.

Then again, he might have gone to seek a reconciliation with Rhiannon, or, more alarmingly, to issue taunts outside the business premises of her current husband.

I think I'd better go and look for him, don't you readers? But, before I do, let me just take a moment to tell you the full sad story of Ken's doomed marriage to Rhiannon. Well, it won't be quite the full story because I don't know the full story. Tell you what, I'll begin the story at the point it became doomed, which was undoubtedly on *New Faces* in '73 – the day of Ken's ill-advised appearance. As you know, Ken did that silly face to camera for which Tony Hatch crucified him, and, utterly embarrassed by the episode, Rhiannon divorced Ken and began a new life with a builder called Martin from Stoney Middleton.

That's a place I must visit when I begin my search for Ken. It boasts an impressive lovers' leap, you see, which Ken, in his desperate state, may have been drawn to. I do hope not. By all accounts, the footpath leading to the leap is ridiculously steep and composed of loose shale, making access highly dangerous. It wasn't always so – in it's heyday couples were literally queuing up to leap off. (Perhaps that's why a

'No photos, please!' Ken Worthington in a private moment.

second lovers' leap was opened near the first, and for a time the two leaps operated in tandem.)

Anyhow, let me get back to my story. Well, rather than letting Rhiannon go, Ken developed a pathological interest in the couple, following her and Martin everywhere they went. One of their earliest dates was a cinema outing to see *Ice Station Zebra*. Ken somehow found out the details and followed them there, sitting a few rows behind them – sorry, I mean in front. (Naturally, being a courting couple, they were on the back row, so he couldn't have been behind them, could he, unless he was standing with the usherette, and that's illegal, surely.) Anyway, Ken was there all afternoon because they saw the film three times in a row – well, you could do then.

Rhiannon and Martin's next date took them to the Sheffield heats of *It's A Knockout* at Arbourthorne playing fields, and, sure enough, Ken was there keeping a low profile. That can't have been easy. An unaccompanied single man in the midst of a large family crowd – with no one to turn to and exchange a guffaw during particularly hilarious moments – would surely have stuck out like a sore thumb. But wait. Aren't we forgetting something? Ken isn't very tall, remember. Even with platform shoes on, his afro would have barely risen above the berets of the Brownie pack he was hiding behind.

Ken has told me privately that his eyeline that day was poor, and that he feels bitter he was only able to get occasional glimpses of the canoodling couple. But I have no sympathy with him. Why the heck didn't he knock it on the head for the day and enjoy the splendid free entertainment on offer? Perhaps he tried to, but couldn't see that very well either. (Surely he could have just cocked his head to one side and listened to Stuart Hall's mad-cap commentary.)

The following year Ken attended Rhiannon and Martin's wedding. But not as a guest. Oh, no. He viewed the proceedings crouched behind a tombstone. That's another locality to which Ken may have been drawn.

(I'd really better go and look for him in a minute actually. I'll just finish my story first.) And, of course, it follows that he was waiting for the newly-weds as they arrived at their secret honeymoon location – a travel lodge on the Dronfield Bypass. Ken was hiding in a Christmas tree plantation. (They were only young saplings, but, with Ken being so small, they more than amply screened him in the thickening twilight.)

Ken's plan was to wait until they'd entered the motel with their bags then creep into the car park to let down the tyres on Martin's Land Rover. But the plan backfired. Martin came out again unexpectedly and caught Ken committing the deed. Ken thought 'Oo, I've had it now' because Martin was a big bloke, and a third degree black sash to boot.

But, rather than being angry, Martin dealt gently with Ken. He seemed to be offering him an olive branch, and said 'It must be terrible for you, Ken. I feel really sorry for you', and Ken thought 'Oo, I've got a right softie here. Maybe I should tackle him.' But then Martin said 'But if I ever see you again, Ken, I'll pull your head off your body!' Ken took fright at that, and started scurrying down the drive back to the bypass. He was skidding all over the place, because it was a bit frosty and he was wearing his Cuban heels as you'd expect.

Poor Ken. It must have been an awful period for him. I've written a song in which I tried to capture what he must have been going through. It'd work well in a musical about the Industrial Revolution. (With this in mind, I sent a cassette copy of the song to all the theatres in the region. That was a couple of years ago. I must get in touch and see what's happening.) Anyhow, here is a fragment of that song to whet your appetite:

Poor Ken, Poor Ken
He's all on his own a-gain
Poor Ken, Poor Ken
His spirit has been bro-ken

Because it had, you know. Since then Ken has struggled to form a meaningful relationship with other ladies – so far with little success. I count my blessings that I've got someone special in my life who'll never abandon me. Or have I?

'What do you mean, John?' I hear you say. 'Has something happened at home which you've not told us about?'

Ken attending his father's funeral in 1952. (That's him – second from the right. He doesn't look very happy, does he!)

Well, yes, it has. And I'm fully prepared to tell you what it is – in a minute. First, though, I should let you know what happened when I eventually searched for Ken – nothing, i.e., I didn't find him, readers, but it wasn't through want of trying. I decided there was nothing for it but to return home, back to my family, and the more pressing matter of the blocked shower-rose.

To amuse myself during the bus ride back to Sheffield I began to speculate about the different possible interpretations of Ken's SOS message. That's to say, did it really mean 'Save Our Souls', or did Ken intend it as a positive message – a few words of encouragement to help me along in his absence? If so, then it might have meant 'Soldier On Son'. It'd be lovely if it did mean that. But, knowing Ken, I concluded it was more likely to mean 'Sod Off Sunshine', or 'Sick Of Shuttleworth', which, if true, was very hurtful – but at least I needn't be quite so concerned for his welfare as I had been.

But immediately on arriving home, I discovered that SOS meant none of those things. The truth was far more hurtful. SOS meant 'Service Our Shower'. Yes, it's true, I'm afraid. I still haven't gleaned the full facts from Mary. All I know at this stage is that, while I was scouring the countryside in search of Ken, he was round at our house fixing the shower. That's not on, is it – entering another man's house and carrying out a major DIY repair without that man's prior knowledge.

And, to add insult to injury, he did it successfully. How did he reach? He must have straddled the bath with his Cuban heels on. His balance would have been extremely poor. Was Mary by his side throughout, helping to keep him upright? I tried to block out such thoughts by immersing myself in other DIY tasks, but I couldn't.

So, you might be wondering, what have I done to upset Mary, then? And I did promise I'd tell you. Well, I refused to spin the lettuce, readers. It's my job, you see. I've long arms and have perfected a powerful windmill action which guarantees a dry lettuce, yet avoids coating Mary's clean windows with unsightly spray. On any other occasion, I'd have been delighted to oblige my wife, but I'd just twigged

500 Bus Stops

yet another possible definition of SOS, you see, and was in a hurry to leave and get on a bus bound for Sutton on Sea! (I was performing a number in my garage, you see, which required me to hit the wave pad at the end, and that's when I solved the conundrum once and for all.)

Yes, I firmly believe that Sutton on Sea, a small seaside resort in Lincolnshire, is where Ken Worthington is in hiding. (I heard him zoom off in his Honda Civic, you see, seconds after I'd discovered he'd repaired our shower – the sneaky rat!) He rents a chalet there, and it's his retreat in times of personal crisis. And I have to join him so he can help me sort out tonight's big booking in Eyam. It's going to be tight, but if I move quickly there may still be time. But, as I said, I left without spinning the lettuce. Will Mary ever forgive me? I'm not so sure. She may be seeking a divorce even as we speak. I sincerely hope not.

Mind you, we nearly got divorced on the day we married. What happened was Mary took exception to something I said in my reception speech. You see, I used to pick up Mary from work on my Honda 70. (She wasn't a dinner-lady then. This was when she worked at the post office. Not as a sub-postal mistress. No, she wasn't qualified for that. She just sold envelopes and various fancy goods, balloons etc.)

At that time, readers, Mary's hairdo was shaped like a motorcycle helmet (it still is, to some degree). Anyway, one evening I picked her up as normal, but it was getting dark so I couldn't see very well. As I started to drive off, Mary shouted 'Wait! Wait! I haven't got my helmet on!' But I thought she had, you see. Well, I told that story at our wedding, thinking it would be a winner, but, no, it went down very badly. Very badly indeed.

Luckily, Mary forgave me and we spent our honeymoon in Whitby, North Yorks, walking up and down the rugged coastline in our respective cagoules. Cagoules, remember, were a relatively new product – windcheaters still being the public's favourite form of rainwear at that time (apart from the mackintosh and pacamac).

There were many good reasons for the success of the windcheater, although, sitting here racking my brains, I can only think of two. Firstly, they cheat the wind, obviously. Secondly, and more crucially, cloth badges or emblems could be sewn with confidence on the breast, upper sleeve, or, indeed, anywhere on the garment. You try stitching a badge of Beverley Minster to your cagoule – it rips the plastic dreadfully. And it makes you feel very angry with yourself for being so stupid, you know.

What was I on about before I digressed? Oh, aye, our honeymoon. Yes, it was lovely. And, years later, I bought an air freshener from Tesco's called Shoreline Walk. Incredibly, the fragrance recreated almost exactly the smell of Whitby, and brought back the pleasures of our honeymoon. I wrote the following letter to Tesco's and told them so.

500 Bus Stops

SOS

21st August, 1987

Dear Tesco's,
Congratulations!

My wife, Mary, went to Tesco's this morning and came back with a can of your new Shoreline Walk air freshener. Wow! What a product. It has a wonderful scent that fills the whole room even after the briefest of squirts.

Your Spring Bouquet fragrance has been a favourite in this house for years, but, although effective in banishing unpleasant odours of all descriptions, it smells like an air freshener, if you know what I mean. This one doesn't. It really does remind you of a sea breeze. In fact, when my wife first squirted it, we both looked at each other and said 'Whitby'. Whitby, in North Yorks, is where we went for our honeymoon, and much of it was spent tramping up and down the rugged coastline, as there wasn't much else to do in the daytime. (It's quite a lonely place you see, with few amenities.)

Anyway, well done! I just wanted you to know that for my money you've come up trumps with this particular product.

Best wishes to all personnel,

J. Shuttleworth (Mr)

A creative moment outside Ken's chalet in Sutton on Sea, Lincs.

I'm delighted to report that Tesco's swiftly wrote back saying 'Our buyers and product teams work very hard in developing our own label product ranges and it is rewarding to know their efforts are appreciated'. Well, they certainly are, Tesco's, and I thank you once again on behalf of both myself and my wife, Mary, because she is still my wife, readers – you know we're not divorced yet, and it's going to take more than a dispute over a lettuce to split us up.

Guess what – I've found Ken Worthington. As I rightly suspected he was in his chalet in Sutton on Sea. But for a man on holiday Ken seems extremely tense. I know holidays can create tension, but, even so, my hostile reception is puzzling. After he did a runner from the teashop, and the underhand way in which he fixed our shower, it should be me that's cross with Ken, not the other way round, and yet he keeps walking away from me, and shunning all eye contact. I must talk to him to find out what his problem is. Excuse me.

Well, readers, Ken's surliness, I am pleased to report, is the result of a gross misunderstanding.

After a visit to the local funfair, during which Ken repeatedly rammed my dodgem car in an attempt to deny me an audience with him, I persuaded him to join me for a more leisurely ride on the sand train. After much pleading and cajoling, Ken's stance softened and he began to tell me all that had happened to him after our separation in the Eyam teashop. It is a wondrous tale, although it seems, I'm sure you will agree, a little far-fetched at times. (Luckily, I recorded the entire conversation on a mini cassette recorder I'd hidden in my jacket pocket – just in case there were legal repercussions.)

'You were gone a long time, John. I started to feel dizzy, so I ordered an Irish coffee.'

'You ordered several, Ken, by all accounts.'

'Well – I got fed up waiting. In the end I nodded off.'

'I'm not surprised, Ken.'

'The next thing I knew I was lying under the table surrounded by a party of Austrian tourists. I tried to move, but I was trapped. They'd all put their rucksacks around me, you see. Then you came in, and I heard you tell the waitress in a very cocky tone that you'd got yourself a booking – and a new agent by the sound of things.'

'No, Ken, you're wrong. What I said was...'

'Don't interrupt, John. Well, I tried to call out to you, but, by this time someone had taken their sweater off and plonked it on top of my head, so my cries were muffled, and went unanswered. Having said that, I was lovely and cosy, and, after that draughty tent, it was just the sort of environment my body craved, you know, and I'm much better now, thank you – '

'Good, I'm glad to hear it, but listen, Ken – '

'Please, John, let me finish. They were still on their sweets by this time. I thought I was going to be there forever, but I wanted to catch a bit of your show – just to see how you were faring under new management – '

'Ken, can I just say something, please – '

'No you can't. When I finally reached the venue I stood outside and listened. I wanted to go in and watch you, but it would have been too painful. What were you singing? That's right – 'The Power of Love'. I've heard you do that one before, of course, but this time you were note perfect. The amazing thing was you sounded just like Jennifer Rush. How you reached some of those high notes, I'll never know. But one thing was clear, John, my services were no longer required. How could they be when you had a new agent who could make you sing so daintily?'

'Ken – it *was* Jennifer Rush singing.'

'Pardon?'

'Someone must have put it on the jukebox. I wasn't even in the pub. The show's not 'til tonight anyway. I was busy scouring the countryside convinced you'd done yourself a mischief.'

'Why would I do that, John?'

'The SOS, Ken. You wrote it on the back of an unpaid bill. In fact, you owe me a tenner!'

'All right, John, I'll knock if off the tour bill. Hang on, I know what this is. It's the beginning of a poem I wrote while I was waiting for you. But my pen ran out. It goes:

> *So summer has almost had its day*
> *And like a friend has slipped away*

Unfortunately, readers, at that point the tape went quiet, because Ken had gone bright red and faltered – embarrassed at performing his own work. Indeed, such was Ken's ordeal that we've had to return to his chalet so Ken can have a lie-down. But clearly he has been busy in my absence, as I've discovered that poem was merely the first of several Ken has written during my absence. One or two of them are absolute rubbish, but generally the standard is quite high. Perhaps I should tell Ken that, to help boost his confidence in his new hobby.

'Can I just say I think your poems are excellent, Ken.'

'Oh, thank you, John. They've certainly helped me get Rhiannon out of my system. And I'm not so scared to confront my past any more.'

'So I see, Ken.'

(See what you think of this one, readers.)

Hooded axeman I'm sick of you
Disturbing my sleep, now go on 'shoo'!

That one would be nice painted on a tray, or could be a suitable lyric for the Communards or Jake Thackeray, someone like that – don't you think, readers?

Ken seems to have cheered up now, so this might be a good time to switch on my cassette player again and interview him about how to cope with divorce, because we've hardly had any tips on the subject yet, and I suspect some of you may be feeling a bit cheated. So here goes:

How to Cope with Divorce

with Ken Worthington

'Ken, I'd be much obliged if you could give the readers some tips on divorce and how to cope with the aftermath.'

'Oo, John, you spat right on my sunglasses then!'

'I did, didn't I. It was the word "aftermath". It's not easy to say. Sincere apologies, Ken.'

'Yes, I should think so, John!'

'All right, Ken, don't over-react. It was only a bit of spittle. So Ken, divorce – how do you cope with it – because you did, didn't you?'

'No, I didn't actually, John. I didn't cope at all.'

'Oh? I thought you did.'

'No. I tried to take my life.'

'You didn't!'

'I did, yes, but I made the mistake of testing the temperature of the water in the canal.'

'I see. If I can just explain for the benefit of the readers, Ken, after your divorce you moved into a caravan situated on the banks of a canal in the Dronfield Woodhouse area. Is that right?'

'Yes, that's correct, John.'

'And you were down on your luck in a big, big way, Ken.'

'I was, yes, and one night I'd had enough. But, as I say, I tested the temperature of the canal and it was just too cold for me, John.'

'Well – good. We're glad, Ken.'

'Mm – so, instead, I decided to make myself a really nourishing meal. I had just a few things left in the larder, you see – and I put them all into a big pan and made myself a nice meal. I had an early night, got up bright and early in the morning and went for an interview at Eagle Star Insurance. And I got the job.'

'Did you mention *New Faces* in your interview, Ken?'

'Oh, no, I kept quiet about that.'

500 Bus Stops

'Good. Well – can you hear what you're saying, Ken?'

'What, John?'

'You're saying that you did cope with divorce. Don't you see, Ken, it's a success story, isn't it?'

'Oh, I suppose it is, yes.'

'So, thank you for sharing that with us, Ken.'

'Not at all. It's a pleasure, John.'

'Good. I can manage without you now, Ken. Why don't you go and write a poem about being without a partner. If it's good enough I might consider it for inclusion in this chapter.'

'Would you, John, really?'

'Yes, but you'll have to hurry, Ken, and bring it to me before I finish the chapter, or I'll have moved into the next bit, and your poem may never be published.'

'Oo, dear – right. I'll be quick then, John.'

In the meantime, readers…

Enjoy your new-found freedom

When, like Ken, you've got over the initial shock of divorce, and accepted the fact that a certain somebody doesn't love you any more, learn to appreciate your solitary existence. Yes, you've got to eat your tea on your own – which isn't very pleasant, as we've already discussed – but at least when the road-sweeping lorry comes past your house you can put your knife and fork down and rush out to join the local children without fear of reprisals from an angry spouse. You can even walk alongside the vehicle for a few hundred yards chatting to the driver (though that's never easy above the din of that sucking thingy) and point out the odd lolly stick that he may have missed. (Again that's rather pointless as they never go into reverse, do they?)

On your way back into the house you can take your time in surveying the front garden for discarded sweet wrappers, or checking the action of your gate. There'll be no one shouting at you to get back inside. You can

'What's the action?' (In the case of this gate, very poor, I'm sorry to say, and eventually it had to be rehung, I'm afraid.)

leave paint brushes soaking in white spirit overnight on the draining board. You can break your journey to the garden centre by stopping midway for a choc-ice, and, whilst eating it, study the logo on the side of the hot-air balloon hovering above the university.

You can do lots of things. The world's your oyster, basically. In fact, if you think about it long enough, divorce doesn't seem that bad really, does it?

Don't become a Romeo OAP

··

I don't want to be
A Romeo OAP
Ringing girls up for a date
On numbers that begin 0898

That's an extract from a song I wrote for Ken to sing when I thought he was trying too hard. He was always going out to night clubs and discotheques, you see. They may sound like ideal locations to secure a lady companion, but Ken's voice is rather frail (though powerfully shrill when roused) and his clever smooth patter was being utterly lost on the ladies. They couldn't hear him above the music, you see. They'd say 'Speak up!' but to no avail. Ken then changed tack completely and began frequenting the local library (there's always a few widows in there changing their story books) but here Ken was faced with the opposite problem. As soon as he started chatting them up they'd say 'Shush!'. He couldn't win.

Recently Ken has begun to turn to the lonely hearts columns, and this is what I'd recommend you do, readers – if you don't think shouting or whispering is for you! No, but seriously it is a good way to find a partner, as long as you exercise caution. A few weeks ago, Ken spotted an advert that said 'Busty professional lady seeks tall gentleman, ex-forces preferably, no beards, please'.

Well, that's not Ken, is it? He's short, even with his Cuban heels on – although his afro gives him a certain elevation (especially when it's just been washed). True, he did do National Service – for thirteen weeks – but apparently all that involved was ordering sacks of potatoes over the telephone. Oh, and at the time, Ken had a little goatee beard – it's gone now, thank goodness – but do you see what I'm trying to say, readers? He wasn't what this lady was looking for at all.

But Ken didn't care. He was excited by the 'busty' bit, and immediately penned a saucy letter to this lady, full of graphic references to her upper half. Rather pleased with himself, he showed me the letter and then the advert, which I viewed with suspicion. Sure enough, upon closer scrutiny, it became apparent that a t-shaped shred of tobacco (Ken's a smoker, you see) had lodged itself between the 's' and the 'y' of the first word. Suffice it to say, she wasn't a 'busty' professional lady. She was a 'busy' one. Ken was mortified when he realized his error, but took comfort in the fact that she'd probably be too busy to write back and tell him off for being so blue.

But she wasn't. By return of post, Ken received a letter doused in perfume from the 'busy' lady. Far from being cross, she seemed to have taken a shine to Ken, saying things like 'How did you know I was busty?', and 'Do you think you can tame this lioness?' Ken was well in.

500 Bus Stops

But I think the bit about the lioness frightened him, so he didn't write back to arrange a meeting.

Instead, he got in touch with a widow who was 'very, very lonely. Loves gardening, but doesn't have a garden'. I told Ken I thought that two 'verys' were a bit ominous, but he didn't seem to mind – anything rather than meet up with a lioness. I suspect the real reason, though, was that he thought he'd be getting someone to dig his garden for free.

Ken obviously had this romantic vision of being sat in his conservatory reading the paper, and occasionally glancing up to see how she was getting on. But, as I said to Ken, 'That's no basis for a meaningful relationship, is it?'

The lonely lady soon twigged Ken's real motives and, after a couple of visits, stopped calling round, which is why his front garden's currently in such a mess. (He wants to do what we've done at the front – concrete it over. It looks much smarter, and provides standing room for an additional vehicle, which can't be a bad thing, can it?)

Well, I've just been presented with a poem by Ken. From the hopeful beam in his eye, it's clear that he thinks he's made the deadline and that his new work will feature in my book – and he's absolutely right!

'Well done, Ken, and thank you for coming up with a new poem so swiftly. May I quote it in full for the readers, so they'll know how to cope with divorce should their partners leave them?'

'You're very welcome to, John. But it's a very down-beat poem, you know. It might make people a bit depressed.'

'Oo, Ken! I'm not sure I want to include it then. Let me read it through to see if it's suitable.'

Well, readers, I've just read it through and I consider it fit for public consumption, because the message at the end is ever so slightly hopeful.

I feel like the crust of bread everyone despises
Always being rejected for more tasty looking slices
The only consolation for being so forgotten
Is knowing that I'm going to meet another crust at the bottom

'Oo, Ken, that's lovely. In fact, that would fit a piece of music I've been working on. The melody goes round and round in your head keeping you awake at night – well it does me. Perhaps we should collaborate, Ken, and come to some kind of arrangement about percentages, etc.'

'I'd love to, John. But won't you need to discuss it with your agent?'

'I will, Ken.'

'And who's your agent now, John?'

'It's you – you daft chump.'

'Is it? Oh, thank you, John. Well, we'd better get our skates on.'

'Where are we going, Ken?'

'Where do you think? The Plague Village of Eyam. If we hurry we might just make it to the venue in time.'

'Oh, Ken, so I will get to end my tour with a flourish after all. Where's your car parked?'

'I've no idea, John. I came by bus, you see.'

'What do you mean? I saw you leave Sheffield in your Honda Civic.'

'Yes, but then I decided it wasn't a suitable mode of transport for a poet so I got back on the bus. Silly, really, because I'm a bit fed up of buses, aren't you, John?'

'I certainly am, Ken. You fool! How are we going to get to Eyam in time for the show?'

There's only one thing for it, readers. We'll have to get yet another blinking bus. Why, oh why, did Ken sell my Austin Ambassador for scrap? We could have done the whole tour in comfort and style. Buses are all right, but there's no glove compartment in which to stow your travel mints. And you have to pay to ride on them which could present a problem because I spent all my money at the funfair earlier. Ken'll see me right though, I'm sure.

'Have you got any cash, Ken?'

'No, John, I spent it all at the fair. And I can't find my switch card anywhere – '

'Oh dear, Ken. Perhaps it fell out of your bumbag when your donkey bolted?'

'What are we going to do, John?'

I'll tell you exactly what we did, readers. We busked in Mablethorpe's Spanish City to raise the necessary funds and it proved to be the toughest venue of the tour so far. A tragic end to my National Rock Tour of the UK, you might think – and you might be right. Then again you might be very wide of the mark.

The good news is that Ken found a fiver in the lining of his bumbag. So we're now aboard a bus, heading back to Sheffield where I will have the opportunity to patch it up with Mary. (I won't offer to spin the lettuce though as it's sure to be dry by now – well, she'll have eaten it ages ago.) No, but what I will do is suggest a trip to Netto's, or to Texas perhaps, for a new washing-up bowl. That tends to cheer her up.

'What a skinflint!' A tightfisted member of the public turns his back on fine live entertainment in Mablethorpe's Spanish City.

The important thing is not to antagonize her, and this is the final piece of advice I'd give to any person eager to avoid divorce – don't antagonize your partner. Please don't or they might leave you – like Mary left me once after a domestic dispute. Naturally, I wrote a song about the incident which you should study carefully. It's a cautionary reminder of the perils of annoying your loved one.

'Hey have you seen my wife?'
I said 'Hey hey have you seen her?'
She left me after a row
It was over a vacuum cleaner
I said 'What's wrong with a broom?'
And she said something obscener
'Oh, Mary, please come back
And I'll buy you a vacuum cleaner'

You'll be pleased to learn that, unlike Ken's widow, Mary did eventually return, and I bought her a lovely second-hand cylinder model, which she still has to this day!

As we wend our merry way to Eyam (we might only get as far as Sheffield though because it's getting a bit late and, besides, our busking stint had a lovely air of finality about it) – it may be a good time to sit back and relax just a little bit. What better way to do this than through the midi channel of my organ. Yes folks, it's time for…

....

Miditations:

....

How to be happy in a sad, sad world

....

Yet again, a very clever title, is it not? Miditations – relaxation through the midi channel of your organ! Right, let us begin. Actually, if you've got an organ (with midi) at home you can do this exercise with me.

The first thing to do is switch on and locate the Fantasy Flute mode. This is number 43 on my Yahama keyboard, but on yours it might be a different number. If you haven't got a Fantasy Flute mode, then you could try Pearl Drop or even Alpen Horn with a touch of vibrato, but, of course, if it's an inferior model you won't have vibrato. You may not even have Alpen Horn, in which case I don't know what to suggest. I'm afraid I've not got time to deal with special cases at this early stage in the lesson. Sorry, I must crack on.

Now – put on your headphones. This ensures you are isolated from the noisy world outside, and free to concentrate. Plus, you're not interfering with the rest of the family's enjoyment of the telly. But, beware! Employing headphone mode can cause your breathing to become a bit raspy, and excessive saliva is sometimes produced. This could alienate your family – and make you even more miserable and anxious.

When you're ready – and in your own time, please – find an audio lead (phono to 5 din preferably) and plug it into your organ's midi channel (you'll find it round the back somewhere). Then, sitting back – well back please for your own safety and comfort – play your organ and relax!

Oo – hang on a minute. Ken's just woken up from yet another nap. (It's all that sea air making him sleepy, and he's still not fully recovered from his mystery virus.)

'Welcome, Ken – I'm just advising the readers on how to relax.'

'That's nice, John.'

'And, if you don't mind me saying so, Ken, you seem a little bit

'Hoover-go hero!' This is an even better way to unwind (whilst retaining cordial relations with your wife). See page 183 for further details.

keyed up yourself. What you need is some relaxation via my midi channel.'

'Do I indeed?'

'Yes, but I can't seem to get the lead to go in properly. Perhaps we should abandon that idea, and do some hypnotism. Do you fancy that, Ken?'

'Oo – I don't really know, John.'

'Of course you do, Ken. It'll be fine. Lie down, please.'

Luckily, readers, we're already on the back seat of the bus, and we've got it to ourselves, so Ken is at liberty to stretch out fully.

'Ken, I forgot to say – before you lie down, you must loosen any tight-fitting garments you may be sporting.'

Ken is now unzipping his leather jacket and struggling a bit, actually. Has he got his pullover caught in the zip mechanism? No, because he's not wearing a pullover. Underneath his jacket today is a lime green lycra top, which is as smooth as the skin beneath.

'It's citrus, John, my top.'

'I see. No talking please, Ken.'

Ken has now wriggled out of his jacket and, instinctively, has folded it up to use as a cushion for his head.

'It's like Lovejoy's, isn't it, Ken – that leather jacket?'

'Is it, John?'

'It is, Ken. He's got one just like that.'

(Please note, readers, this pre-exercise banter is designed to put the patient at their ease. You can ask them other things like 'Aren't you working today?' or 'What video have you hired for this evening then?' But keep it simple, or they may smell a rat, and do a runner.)

'Now listen very carefully, Ken. Your eyelids are getting heavy – like a ton weight is attached to each of them on a piece of string or, to be absolutely safe, reinforced steel cable. What's the matter, Ken? Close your eyes and relax. Now you are slipping down a dark tunnel. There's no way back, Ken. So, co-operate with me – co-operate with me – that's it, Ken. Hey! What are you doing? Lie down!'

'I'm sorry, John. I don't want to do it any more. I'm frightened.'

'Don't be silly, Ken. You're perfectly safe.'

'No, I don't like it, John. Your face is too close to mine. Are you qualified to do this?'

'Well no, but I'd love to be.'

'I'm sorry, John. I'm going to have to go and sit upstairs.'

'Well, all right, that's a good idea. Let me come with you, Ken. Yes, there'll be better views for us up there – more relaxing.'

'No, John. I'm going alone. I don't feel safe with you.'

'Now you're being offensive, Ken. I'd like you to leave, please.'

'Well, I'm going anyway, John. I'm going – and I don't want you to follow me.'

'I've no intention of doing so. I've got my book to finish.'

'Yes, you have!'

Well – sorry about that, readers. I hope Ken's little outburst hasn't affected your own efforts to acquire a hypnotic state. It wouldn't surprise me if it had. He was being quite disruptive. (Ken'll probably start peering down the periscope now and distract the driver. I've seen him do that before. Well, if he gets thrown off the bus it'll be no less than he deserves.) Now where were we? Oh, yes, I'd like you to sleep on, if you will. 'Sleeep – Sleeeeep onnnn – '

Now, you are in a deep trance, and you will – oopps – no! Wake up, readers! I'm sorry. I've lost my bottle. Ken's right. I'm not qualified to do this. It's dangerous. I'm meddling with forces I don't understand. Sorry. Let's think of another way to relax – I know, I'll sing a relaxing song:

How to be happy in a sad, sad world
It's incredibly easy
And to tell you will please me

Go caravanning in Clwyd or Dyfed
Order a pizza and have it delivered
How to be happy in a sad, sad world

You should be thankful for your lot
The friends and the neighbours you have got
But what if you live in Sarajevo?
Yes, well, fortunately we do not

Visit a friend in a home or a hospice
Go to the zoo and say 'Boo!' to the ostrich
How to be happy in a sad, sad world –

What if there's no ostrich to say boo to? What if it's been transferred to another zoo because it was too aggressive? Does this mean you're condemned to be miserable? No, don't be so stupid. It doesn't have to be an ostrich – I just said that because it rhymes with 'hospice'. Well, nearly. No, it can be any animal of your choosing.

Or, if all the animals are hiding that day, why not visit the coffee shop and enjoy a cafetière? That's the new one, isn't it? (I keep saying campacinno is, but this is even more recent, this one.) Yes, it lacks the luxurious finish of the campacinno (no froth or chocolate droppings), but it certainly looks mightily impressive on your tray. As you carry it to your table, heads will be turning, I guarantee it, especially if you've got a Danish pastry on board, too, with a nice lattice effect. (One word of caution, readers. You do know you have to press the plunger thingy down, don't you? I mean, if you've not had a cafetière before, there's a

This felt-tip pen study of 'man in a garden' by Karen Shuttleworth, aged 6, may also help you to relax. Then again, you may (as Ken did) find it horribly disquieting.

danger you'll leave it up because you've assumed its sole function is to keep the coffee warm. That's an easy mistake to make – though one you will never repeat, I assure you.)

Well, we've still a fair way to go before we reach Sheffield so let me give you some more advice on how to be happy in a sad, sad world.

Voluntary work

The following extract from a recent composition of mine, the calypso-based 'I Want To Be A Community Leader' pinpoints exactly my own involvement in the voluntary sector.

> *I supervise ping-pong at the drop-in centre*
> *I've a tiny little office which no one else may enter*
> *Unless an injury has been sustained*
> *Then they can whilst I administer first aid*

It's true, you know. That's what I do every Thursday night, and it's highly rewarding work. Incidentally, next week we're holding a 'gunge-athon' to raise money to buy a couple of sponge bats. We've currently only got hard ones, you see.

Charity work

This is similar to voluntary work, but with the added bonus that you sometimes get to dress up and be silly. But be careful. I once turned up at our local swimming baths dressed as a Cromwellian foot soldier because I'd heard there was going to be a massacre re-enacted in the deep end. (It was a fun event, you see, to raise funds for a water heater in a gents' hostel.)

But, when I got there, everyone was in their trunks. I'd only gone and got my dates mixed up. But I stayed for a while to watch the antics, which was a big mistake. Within seconds, this lad with a ginger flat top

500 Bus Stops

started doing karate chops in the water and trying to grab my pike. To be fair to him, he was doing it good-naturedly but I was getting soaked – and it was a hired costume, you see – so I went to chat to Tony, the lifeguard, who was having a cigarette in his office.

You won't know this, but Tony dreams of becoming a paramedic (mind you, who doesn't!). He's the man who introduced me to shower gel, you know. I don't know about you, but I was very wary of the product and had been ever since its launch in the early eighties. To me, it always resembled Swarfega. So it was a fantastic surprise to discover from Tony that actually it's lovely and frothy, and produces the creamiest of lathers when rubbed vigorously on to the torso or legs.

Enjoy your job

I'd love to, but, as you know, readers, I'm currently unemployed. I was hoping this tour would change all that, but what if Mary's right and that elusive recording contract never materializes? Ken says I mustn't panic, it'll take a while for the success of the tour to filter through to the public consciousness, but perhaps it would be wise to seek paid employment outside the entertainment industry, just in case.

But, as Mary says, who'd have me? I'm no spring chicken, as you know. I think Homebase might be glad of my services. I'm handy with a saw, and I'm as familiar with the layout of the store as any current employee, I'd imagine. And, whilst fawn remains my favourite colour, I'd be more than happy to don a pair of those lovely green dungarees. Mm – maybe I'll pop in tomorrow with my CV.

I've still not heard about a job I applied for several years ago. It's a shame because it sounded quite interesting. Here now is the letter I wrote (the last of my collected letters, I'm afraid, readers).

26th May, 1994

Premier Poultry,
Recruiting Department.

Dear Miss Wright,
I wish to apply for the position of Bird Intake Manager at your poultry factory in Scunthorpe. I have good communication skills and am very strong and positive. Also I am numerate, having assisted my daughter, Karen, with her maths homework on several occasions when she was close to tears with sines and cosines, which are quite tricky for the novice. (She came 11th in recent tests, which she admits was largely due to my help.)

If successful, I understand I'll be responsible for the welfare of the birds when they arrive at the factory. But could you tell me please: Are they dead already or still alive at this point? If they're still alive I imagine I'll have to try and calm them down, and possibly provide activities to distract them from thinking about what's going to happen to them, or do we trick them into believing they're not going to die but will be soon released into the countryside to roam freely? I'm not sure what your existing policy is, but that sounds like quite a clever idea to me.

I'm currently unemployed, but I do cut the grass once a fortnight for a halfway house that's just opened near us. (They haven't got a mower yet, you see, and in return I borrow their electric typewriter for my job applications which I have done for this one – as you can see!)

Yours faithfully,

John Shuttleworth (Mr)

500 Bus Stops

Not that I've been idle since being made redundant as a security guard. I have, as you know, kept myself busy writing songs and honing my lyrics – and I've learned how to:

Make effective use of leisure time

These days, we are faced with a lot more free time than previously, aren't we? Well, I am, and it's important that we don't squander these periods of leisure. Don't just sit watching the telly – plan your viewing strategically, marking with a big star those programmes which must be viewed that evening, and, with a little star – or a heart, if you want to – the programmes which can be taped and watched in the morning.

Familiarize yourself thoroughly with the remote control; be confident you can locate the volume button swiftly and painlessly, in case you have to turn the sound down when your relations arrive unexpectedly.

How to create a lovely home environment

Keep your house spick and span and you'll go around with a big grin on your face all day long – well, you might do. Obviously, if you get some bad news during the day you're going to be devastated, but there's nothing you can do about that at this stage. Whatever you do, don't plan for these awful bombshells. They'll come sooner or later. In the meantime, think positive. Get that vacuum cleaner out, and wipe down the surfaces in the kitchen – unless they've already been wiped.

Wait! Come back into the lounge again for a second, if you will. Stand in the centre of the room and – taking care not to crick your neck – look all around you. The carpet may be vacuumed, the coffee table gleaming, but – are all your videos correctly labelled, neatly stacked, and available for immediate access? Are any of them upside down?

Look again. Are there any books lying around? If so, have you considered storing them in a big box in the loft to give to your children when they finally leave home. If you're going to read them then fine, leave them in the bookcase. But, let's be honest. When will you find the time? Answer: you won't. Or, why not consider doing what they do in posh pubs and carveries, i.e., stick them together with a strong adhesive. This prevents curious visitors from taking them out and having a nose. Remember, you paid a lot of money for the complete set. They arrived in a pristine condition. Why shouldn't you be allowed to keep them that way?

I was in a pub once on the outskirts of Goole – that's getting towards the East coast, isn't it, Goole? Well, not that near, I suppose. Anyway, I was thoroughly enjoying my mixed grill until this woman with fuzzy hair – a bit like Cleo Laine's – strolled up to the bookcase and, without warning, took a book out and started reading it. Bizarrely, the management had failed to glue the books together. Well, now they were paying the price. Luckily, the barman saw her, dashed over and told her to put it back. It could have turned very nasty. Well, they were for display only, weren't they, and it was sickening to see somebody abusing the system in that way.

Don't forget to make your bed in the morning, and hang your slacks up, please, etc. Erm – place your face flannel over the edge of the bath after you've washed your face. But do make sure the rest of the household are aware it's still in daily use. A few weeks back I started getting an itchy face, and I couldn't work out why until I confided in Mary, and discovered the grizzly truth. She had been using my flannel to clean the bath, and, consequently, had been sprinkling it generously with Vim. I can laugh about it now, but at the time I was hopping mad!

Did you have an unhappy childhood?

I've thought of one reason why you might be feeling tense and unable to relax – your childhood may have been fraught with misery. You see, Ken Worthington had a miserable childhood. You witnessed earlier how

'That's better!' The true path to inner contentment requires you to do nothing more than sit staring out of the window whilst your dinner goes down. (Blinking obvious really!)

keyed up he gets when things aren't going his way, and you must agree that some of his behaviour during my tour has been extremely erratic. Well, I put it down to a catalogue of childhood disasters that warped his mind and left him feeling permanently anxious, and inexplicably blue.

When Ken was little his parents ran a pub, and one day he fell off a bar stool in the Snug, and everybody sort of went 'Ooo!' because they thought he was injured, I presume. He wasn't. He got up and walked away from the incident.

But Ken is convinced it affected him in the long term. Overnight he became quite aggressive and started carrying a pocket penknife which he used to stick into people if they crossed him. He began gouging out bits of mortar everywhere he went. In the Peak District he was thwarted in his mission, because it's all dry stone walls there, of course, so he'd just sit on the wall and kick his legs to and fro. (Mind you, even that's going to harm the stone eventually, isn't it?)

As if things weren't bad enough, Ken started to wake up in a cold sweat and see a hooded axeman at the end of his bed. Ugh! A hooded axeman at the end of your bed. Imagine that. But perhaps Ken brought on the apparition himself by reading war comics before he retired – *Captain America*, that sort of thing. I used to read *Tufty* and had a lovely night's sleep!

Doreen Melody is another one who has let unfortunate incidents affect her, in a most unsavoury fashion. Doreen – a friend of my wife, Mary – quit the armed forces recently, and when she left was medically downgraded. This has left her feeling very bitter, and she screws her face up a lot more than she used to at receiving any kind of bad news. For example, if she hears it's going to be misty tomorrow, or upon being told the lamb has just all gone at the garden centre café.

But it's Doreen's own fault, because she's a chain-smoker, and she's got a very bad posture. (To look at her you wouldn't think she was once a soldier.) Having said that, she's got a fantastic camper van. It's got a sturdy chrome ladder which gives direct access to the roof. (See the picture on page 146.)

You'd think owning such a fabulous vehicle would have mellowed Doreen, and helped her to cope with life's knocks, but no. A few weeks ago, I went to the Crosspool Tavern for an early drink with Mary and Doreen. At one point, I reached for Mary's drink – because she couldn't reach it, you see – and Doreen snapped 'Gerroff, John, that's mine!' All right, fair enough, I'd made a mistake. But then Doreen whispered in my ear 'Just remember, John, that at any moment I could kill you with a single punch'. All right, she was quite drunk, but, still, you don't say things like that, do you?

500 Bus Stops

nº 186

I could have turned out bitter and twisted, because I had some unpleasant things happen to me when I was little. When I was seven I was invited to a little lass's party in the village of Great Hucklow, you know, near the gliding club. I kept seeing shadows of the gliders flicker across the lawn, but that wasn't the nasty experience. I found that quite pleasant. During the course of the birthday tea, I ate a fairy cake. (Nothing nasty about that either, but hang on, I haven't finished my story.) Well, when I'd eaten the cake, I started to eat the wrapper. I thought it was rice paper, you see. But it wasn't. It was a wax-based, greaseproof paper, and I was spitting the bits out all over the floor. I got a little smack for that, but – and this is the point I'm trying to make – I didn't let it affect me.

Perhaps that's not a very extreme example. All right, what about this one? In the village of Bamford, Derbyshire, where I spent my formative years, lived this lad – Hugo, I think he was called. A bit posh he was – he wore shorts until he was about fourteen. Mind you, you did then. There was nothing funny about that. Well, when I was about five, Hugo used to play this trick on me, repeatedly. And I fell for it every time.

He'd see me in the garden with my little stick and shout across 'John! Come here. I've got a sweetie for you. Close your eyes and open your mouth'. So I'd do that – be like a little bird, you know, all expectant – then he'd shove leaves and twigs in my mouth, and other assorted detiritrius.(Mm, maybe Ken's right and it is demetrius after all.) Then he'd throw his head back and laugh at the sky. Sometimes I'd laugh as well – if I got the joke. But usually I used to cry, because I wanted a sweetie. In fact, I wouldn't mind one now, because the air's a bit arid here on the bus, and I've run out of Werther's. (I know for a fact that Ken's got a packet of Revels, but I'm not traipsing upstairs cap in hand. Ken's still in my bad books, remember.)

What I'm trying to say, readers, is that, even at that tender age, I was aware of my own mortality. Death didn't frighten me because I knew I could die at any moment – as indeed I could now if the bus were to crash – though being on the top deck Ken's surely more at risk than me.

(Hopefully I'd just suffer minor cuts and whiplash.) You could drop dead without warning too, of course, even while reading this book. But please, for heaven's sake, readers, don't get all panicky and start rushing through the final few pages just so that, in your last dying breath, you can say 'I finished it! I finished it!'. That would be downright barmy.

Once, I attended the funeral of a man called Eric Blackburn. He ran a camping shop – before he died, obviously – and he did very poor business – only used to sell approximately one tent a fortnight. I was in his shop once – returning a trailer I'd borrowed to move some unsightly white rocks from our garden – and during the two hours I was there he had only one customer, a little lad who bought a pair of mittens. Mind you, Eric seemed quite happy with that. And he must have had a bob or two, because he had a Volvo, and he had a hang-glider, because that's how he died.

He was coming in to land up on Burbage Moor – near Hathersage, this is – and he said 'Get the Volvo, Val!' as he made his final approach. Those were his last words, apparently, to his wife (or indeed, anybody). A freak gust of wind suddenly took him off again, and he got his wellingtons caught in some ferns. This sent him off at an awkward angle. He crashed into a rock, and died as a result of his injuries.

Now, I attended his funeral, and came home to find my son, Darren, poorly on the sofa. He had tonsillitis, and was seeing little creatures on the ceiling – like you do when you've got a fever. At that time, we had a caravan parked hard up against the bay window of the lounge, so there was very little natural daylight coming into the room. It was like a tomb, even on a bright sunny day, which it was that afternoon. All this, and Darren's sickness (and I think Kirsty had a bad leg), increased my melancholy, and I suddenly became very aware of the mortality of the Shuttleworth family.

I wrote a song about my feelings, which I still maintain would work very well in a summer pageant or a Forces' revue show, something like that. Perhaps I should offer it to Doreen Melody. But I hesitate to because (a) she's no longer in the army, (b) she's got a very raspy voice, with poor command of vibrato, and (c) it's a gentleman's lyric.

I'll sing it to you now, if I may. As the words wash over you, you will become more aware of your own mortality, and thereby more able to cope with Death, as it approaches, which I'm afraid it will before too long. (Unfortunately, as you can't really hear me singing in this book, you'll have to imagine the gorgeous melody.)

> *I will attend you when you're very ill*
> *Plump the pillows beneath your head*
> *I'll undertake your burial*
> *Or my wife Mary will*
> *If I'm already dead*
>
> *Hush now my child, lie you very still*
> *Eat your tomato soup*
> *And soft white bread*
> *For I'll undertake your burial*
> *Or my wife Mary will*
> *If I'm already dead*
>
> *Oh-ho, oh-ho –*
> **(It should be like Kate Bush, this bit.)**
>
> *Oh-ho –*

Cheer up – it might not happen

Did you like that lyric? It's a bit maudlin, really, isn't it, and perhaps not a good note to end my book on – and I will have to sign off fairly shortly, I'm afraid. We're on the outskirts of Sheffield now, and Ken has come downstairs to prepare for our getting off. (He's not established eye contact with me, though.) He's sitting at the front near the driver on one of those high seats that you should really keep free in case an old lady gets on.

Tell you what – I'll tell you a joke:

Receptionist: 'Doctor Billabong will see you now.'

Patient: 'Which doctor?'

Receptionist: Oh, no, he's fully qualified.'

Did you like that? It's simple, yes, but clever, and not the slightest bit blue. All right, what about this one?

Question: What road is made of paper?

Answer: The A4.

Question: What road is made of even more paper?

Answer: The A3.

That's not the funniest joke in the world, perhaps, but it must have raised a slight chuckle. I hope it did because that's one of mine, you know. I made it up whilst driving on the A365 – the road to Chapel-en-le-Frith. But it's not made of paper that road, obviously!

If you're still feeling down in the mouth, why not pay somebody a nice compliment. You'll brighten up their day at least, and, who knows, your kindness might have far wider repercussions than you'd ever dreamed possible.

I always remember at junior school once we had to do a project on Georgian town life. This involved everybody in the class drawing a sedan chair. Now, mine was brilliant. That sounds like I'm boasting, I realize, but seriously it was very, very good. It had a little man inside, and shading and everything. I traced it, yes, but even so. The boy in the desk next to mine, Robert, kept looking at it and saying 'Cor, that's brilliant that, John!' and it was, you know.

Now, then, I looked across at his sedan chair and, honestly, it was rubbish. I couldn't tell what it was. It looked like a camel or something. And I don't know why it was so bad because he'd traced his as well. But, rather than be nasty, I tried to look for the positive things in it. I said 'Nice use of colour' – things like that, because, to be fair, he had used his colours quite nicely.

Well, he puffed his little chest out with pride and said 'Oh thanks,

John!'. And you know, I'm so glad I said what I did because now he's Senior Architect for Derbyshire County Council!

I'm looking forward to seeing my kids. Karen should be in her bedroom now doing her homework, but she's more likely to be sitting on the wall outside the dry cleaner's with her friend, Maxine. You might be thinking that's not a very interesting place for two teenage girls to spend their evening – outside a dry cleaner's. But, you'd be missing the point again, readers.

What draws them there is not the shop but the wall itself. True, the bright fluorescent lighting in the shop is handy in that it casts enough light outside for Maxine to light her cigarettes by. Yes, unfortunately that young lady is a smoker. Karen isn't, thankfully, although once when I was driving past I saw her giggling as Maxine struggled to light up – which is a worrying sign.

Darren definitely won't be in. By now he'll be two thirds of the way through his shift at Victoria Wine. As to what his plans are after work, I really wouldn't like to speculate – although when I passed him on the landing earlier in the day (before I left to go to Sutton on Sea), he was clutching a rented copy of *Top Gun*. It's quite possible that he plans to view the Tom Cruise blockbuster upon his return from work. Then, again, he may have already watched it, in which case the tape will be back on the shelves and available once again for public hire.

Oh, no! I've just realized something – Mary won't be home either. She'll have gone to Bums, Tums and Thighs at the Methodist Hall with Doreen, so the house'll be deserted. Oo, I don't fancy going home to an empty house, and I suspect Ken won't either (though being a lone bachelor it's a situation he must surely be well used to).

Hey, I've just had a thought – we could miss our stop, stay on the bus and carry on to the Plague Village of Eyam where I could perform my final booking of the tour, as originally planned. Well, we could, but I'm a bit tired to be honest – I've done a heck of a lot of travelling today, and so has Ken.

What might be a better plan is to alight a couple of stops before

Eyam, and have a lager or two in Baslow. They do bar snacks now – garlic mushrooms, that sort of thing, and a little basket of bread appears without being requested. I fancy that myself, and I've a hunch that Ken might, too – although, initially, he may display some resistance to the idea.

I'm going to join him on the long seat and put forward my suggestion. Bye for now, readers. (Oo, thanks for reading my book, by the way!)

'Who's that then?'